# DWELLERS IN DARKNESS

# DWELLERS
# IN DARKNESS

*An Introduction to the Study of Termites*

BY

## S. H. SKAIFE
D.Sc., F.R.S.S.Af.

ILLUSTRATED
BY THE AUTHOR

## LONGMANS GREEN AND CO
LONDON · NEW YORK · TORONTO

LONGMANS, GREEN AND CO LTD
6 & 7 CLIFFORD STREET LONDON W I
BOSTON HOUSE STRAND STREET CAPE TOWN
531 LITTLE COLLINS STREET MELBOURNE

LONGMANS, GREEN AND CO INC
55 FIFTH AVENUE NEW YORK 3

LONGMANS, GREEN AND CO
20 CRANFIELD ROAD TORONTO 16

ORIENT LONGMANS LTD
CALCUTTA BOMBAY MADRAS
DELHI VIJAYAWADA DACCA

*First Published* 1955
*Second Impression* 1956

PRINTED IN GREAT BRITAIN
SPOTTISWOODE, BALLANTYNE AND CO. LTD.
LONDON AND COLCHESTER

# PREFACE

THERE has been a marked growth of interest in the social insects, bees, wasps and ants, in recent years and several excellent books have been written about them, but comparatively little has been published about the most ancient and most challenging of them all, the termites. It is hoped that this book will help to fill the gap. For the past twenty years I have been able to devote much of my time to the study of a species of termite that is common on the mountain slopes near Cape Town, and the results of these investigations are given in this book, in plain, everyday language. Ways and means had to be devised of keeping them in observation nests in the laboratory and these are described in the hope that others will be induced to take up the study of the fascinating little creatures that are commonly called "white ants," that are widely spread over the warmer parts of the world, that are of such great economic importance and that offer so many baffling problems.

The detailed account given in this book of the strange ways of the black-mound termite of the Cape is entirely new because this particular species has never been studied before. In fact, the habits of the higher termites are scarcely known at all because hitherto they have not been made the subject of laboratory investigations owing to the difficulty of keeping them alive under artificial conditions. The more primitive wood-inhabiting termites are better known, but we still have a great deal to learn about them all. Entomologists who are looking for fresh fields to conquer might well consider these lowly relatives of the cockroach that have learned to live in highly complex communities in their dark, fortress homes. The apparatus described at the end of this book is simple, inexpensive and easy to construct, and any amateur or professional biologist could repeat and extend the work with other species of termites.

S. H. SKAIFE

Cape Town,
*March*, 1954

# CONTENTS

# CONTENTS

# LIST OF PLATES

There are also a number of illustrations in the text.

*Chapter One*

# THE MOST ANCIENT COMMUNITIES

THE only creatures on this earth, besides man, that have learned to live together and co-operate in highly organised communities are the social insects, ants, bees, wasps and termites. Of these, man has been in existence as a social animal for less than one million years; ants, bees and wasps for about seventy million years; and termites for something like two hundred million years. Thus the termitary is by far the oldest type of community to be found on the face of the globe and it is also the one about which we know the least.

Although termites are often spoken of as "white ants," they are not white and they are not ants. They are much more primitive in their structure and development than ants, and their nearest relatives are cockroaches, which are also of very ancient origin. We know little about termites because they are perhaps the most difficult of all insects to study in a living state in the laboratory. For countless generations they have lived under sheltered conditions inside their fortress homes that are called "ant-heaps" in Africa. The rays of the sun never reach them, no breeze ever stirs the still atmosphere of their corridors, no rain ever falls upon them, the air they breathe is always humid and highly charged with carbon dioxide, and they are not exposed to extremes of temperature. They are literally "Dwellers in Darkness," quite shut off from the outside world. As a result of this sheltered existence they are extremely delicate and die quickly when removed from their natural environment. Furthermore, they can only survive when crowded together in dense throngs. No solitary termites are known.

Consequently living termites have been but little studied in the laboratory and such investigations as have been carried out have been limited mostly to primitive species that live in small colonies in timber. They have, however, been collected assiduously enough, preserved in alcohol and described and named. T. E. Snyder, the American authority on termites, in his *Catalog of the Termites of the World*, published in 1949 by the Smithsonian Institution, gives a list of all the species known to science up to that date and it includes 1,861 living and 68 fossil species, 1,929 altogether. Nearly all of these are found only in tropical and sub-tropical regions, but a few small, insignificant species have penetrated as far north as the Mediterranean region of Europe and to the borders of the United States and Canada. The continent of Africa seems to be their headquarters, with 396 species known to occur south of the Sahara.

Fossil ants, bees and wasps have been found in rocks of the early part of the Tertiary Period, the Eocene. At this period of the earth's history, about seventy million years ago, flowers were already in existence—bees could not have evolved without them —and most of the modern genera of birds had already appeared. Numerous fossil insects, beautifully preserved in amber of the Lower Oligocene, have been found and named and these include flying termites that are little different from those we know to-day. These fossils show that termites were much more widely spread on the earth's surface then than they are now and they prove that, at this remote period, winged termites left their nests on nuptial flights somewhere in the region where the Baltic Sea is to-day. Some of them got caught in resin oozing from the trunks of giant coniferous trees and were thus preserved, much in the same way as the scientist of modern times preserves his specimens by mounting them in Canada balsam on microscope slides.

There are shales found in Colorado in the United States that are believed to have been formed from volcanic ash that fell into a lake long ago and these contain many fossil insects, including termites. It would seem, then, that in this area many millions of years ago, some flying termites were caught and overwhelmed by a shower of ash from an active volcano in the vicinity whilst they were on their nuptial flight. Similar fossils have been found in other parts of the world, including more recent ones in gum copal, the hardened gummy exudation from a tropical tree that is still in existence. Gum copal is not as old as amber and is found in Pleistocene formations, laid down during the age of man.

Fossils of worker termites have so far been found only in more recent rocks of the Pleistocene period, but this does not prove that they were only evolved as late as this. The flying adults are much more likely to fall into lakes or bogs or to get entangled in sticky exudations from trees than are the workers burrowing in the soil or in timber. Their wings and hard, chitinous skeletons are more likely to be preserved than the soft-bodied, wingless workers. Also the fossils in amber and shales seventy million years old are very similar to modern flying termites and it is reasonable to assume that they had similar habits and lived in communities with workers and soldiers, like the present-day termites.

But there is one fossil that takes the history of termites much further back than the Eocene. This is the clear impression of a wing, only about three-quarters of an inch long, found in fine-grained shale in the middle-Permian deposits of the Sylva River Basin in the Ural Mountains. This was described and figured by the Russian scientist, G. Zalessky, in 1937, and he named it *Uralotermes permianum*. The form and venation of the wing appear to be undoubtedly those of an ancient termite, with affinities to cockroaches found as fossils in rocks of similar age and older. Cockroaches are among the most ancient of all insects, fossils having been found in Carboniferous rocks some three hundred million years old and it seems certain that the origin of termites goes back nearly as far. The structure of the bodies, the development, and even the intestinal parasites of the two are so similar that they are obviously close relatives.

The Russian fossil shows, then, that some two hundred million or so years ago, there were flying termites feebly fluttering on their wedding flight amid sombre conifers and tree-ferns, long before there were any flowers or butterflies or bees or birds or mammals upon earth, in that far distant age when giant reptiles flourished. In all probability the worst natural enemies the flying termites had to face in those far-off days were huge dragon-flies a foot or more in length.

Compared with termites, man is an upstart of yesterday, and even the ants, bees and wasps are comparative newcomers. With two hundred million years behind them, termites have evolved a grimly efficient organisation in which the individual has no rights at all and everything is run for the good of the community as a whole. Like all social insects, they are ruthless totalitarians and the sub-title of this book might well be "A Study of Totalitarianism in Nature."

Let us take a look inside the termitary and see what life there is like.

*Chapter Two*

## THE ABODE OF PERPETUAL NIGHT

FIRST of all, let us get the systematic position of the insects we are about to study quite clear. Termites are placed in a group, or order, by themselves known to entomologists as the *Isoptera*, a name which means "equal-winged" and which is given to them because the two pairs of wings of the flying adults are of the same size and similar in appearance. This group is placed low down in the classification of insects, near the orders that include cockroaches, grasshoppers, crickets and earwigs, and it is far removed from the order of more highly developed insects, the *Hymenoptera*, that includes ants, bees and wasps.

The *Isoptera* are divided into five families. The lowest of these, the *Mastotermitidæ*, includes only one primitive species found in Australia that differs from all the others in being more cockroach-like in the form of its hind wings and other characters. The next family is the *Kalotermitidæ*, widely spread over the world and including some 223 species of primitive termites that live in small colonies in dead timber. It is a few members of this family that have so far been the main subjects of laboratory studies in the United States and Europe; the other families have hitherto been scarcely studied at all in observation nests. Then comes the *Hodotermitidæ*, a small family of only 30 species that includes the destructive harvester termites of Africa. Next is the *Rhinotermitidæ*, with 147 species, most of which live in subterranean nests; the colonies of some of them reach a large size and a few species are of considerable economic importance because of the damage they do to timber in buildings. Finally, there is the *Termitidæ*, the highest and by far the largest of all the families, and the least known. This includes no less than 1,323 species, among which are some of the most destructive of all termites, the fungus-growers of Africa.

The black-mound termite of the Cape, which is the main subject of this book, is known to science as *Amitermes atlanticus* Fuller, and is a member of the last-named family. So far it has been recorded only from the south-west corner of the Cape Province of the Union of South Africa, but it belongs to a large genus of no less than 76 species widely spread over the world, and what is said about it here will probably be found to apply also to other members of the group. Of the 76 *Amitermes* species, 29 are found in Africa, 27 in Australia, 7 in North America, 7 in South America, 3 in India and Malaya and 3 in the Mediterranean region. Many of them construct nests similar to those of the black-mound termite, but some have subterranean homes, whilst one Australian species, *Amitermes meridionalis* Froggatt, is responsible for what are probably the most extraordinary structures built by insects anywhere in the world. These are the famous compass mounds found in the Port Darwin area, wedge-shaped, reaching a height of twelve feet and a length of ten feet, and always placed so that they point north and south. It is probable that these termites orientate their homes in this way in order to obtain protection from the fierce heat of the midday sun. The long, flat sides of the mounds, facing east and west, receive the rays of the sun in the morning and afternoon, when the warmth is acceptable, but at high noon the rays strike only the narrow edge of the wedge and the mounds do not get over-heated. When one remembers that these fortresses are built by feeble, blind insects only about one-fifth of an inch long, one cannot fail to be filled with amazement.

The nests of the black-mound termite of the Cape are not as remarkable as those of the Australian compass termite, yet they are interesting enough and well worthy of study. On the rugged mountain slopes of the Cape Peninsula small black mounds may be seen dotted about amid the proteas, heaths and bulbous plants for which this area is famous. They are numerous in some parts where the soil is sandy, but absent in others and they are rarely found on clayey soil. The largest of them are only about two feet high by two feet in diameter at the base and they are hemispherical or conical in shape (Plates I and II).

Although the soil on which they are found is white or grey or yellow, the mounds are always dark grey or black. This is because the termites use their excrement as the rapid-hardening, weatherproof cement for building their homes and their ex-

PLATE I

(*a*) The nest of the black-mound termite, *Amitermes atlanticus*
This mound is about twenty years old. The coin at the base is half-a-crown, to show comparative size.

(*b*) A mound sawn in half to show internal structure
The cells communicate one with the other by small circular openings about one-sixteenth of an inch in diameter. There is no royal cell.

PLATE II

(*a*) A nest of the black-mound termite, with six-inch nails inserted
in it to measure the rate of growth

This mound, about two feet high, is twenty-five or more years of age

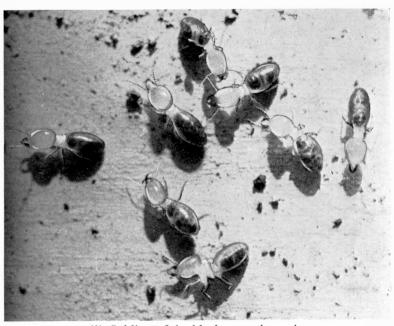

(*b*) Soldiers of the black-mound termite

They are about one-fifth of an inch long, sterile males and females, and
quite blind

cretions blacken anything with which they come in contact. If you think for a moment, you will realise that the sewage problem inside the densely crowded community must be a difficult one and the insects have solved it in a bizarre but efficient manner. As will be explained later, the food passes through the alimentary canal of several individuals until all the nourishment has been extracted from it and only a dark-coloured sticky paste is left. This, together with particles from the soil, is used as their building material when constructing or repairing their fortress homes. The mixture dries quickly and is very strong; even the heavy winter rains at the Cape make no impression on the stout walls and it takes a good blow from a hatchet to break the mound open. A heavy man can jump on it without doing any damage.

Except for one brief interval during the year, when the nuptial flight takes place, the mounds show no signs of life at all on the exterior and you will see nothing of the inhabitants unless you make a breach in the walls. The termites live inside in a stygian darkness such as we never know and they shun the light like the plague. They are doomed to live under these conditions, completely shut off from the outside world, because they are such defenceless creatures, blind, slow-moving and soft-bodied, and they are surrounded by their age-long foes, the agile, aggressive ants that would quickly wipe them out if they could get at them. As will be shown later in this book, there is ceaseless, merciless warfare between these two types of insects.

The base of the mound penetrates only three or four inches below the surface of the ground and it is quite easy to remove it whole, complete with inhabitants, and to carry it into the laboratory for study purposes. If it is broken open the interior is found to resemble a large sponge, with innumerable irregular cavities about half an inch to an inch across, each cell communicating with its neighbours by small circular openings only about one-sixteenth of an inch in diameter, holes just big enough for the inmates to creep through from one chamber to the next but that are small enough to be plugged quickly if the outer wall of the fortress is damaged.

Near the exterior of the mound the cells are more or less spherical and the walls are made of sand mixed with excrement.

In the interior the cells are longer and narrower and the walls contain little sand; they consist almost entirely of the hard, dense cement and this part of the nest will burn away to a grey powder if strongly heated. All too often fierce veld fires sweep over the mountain slopes of the south-west Cape and, after these, some mounds may be found that have been completely destroyed by the flames and only heaps of fine red powder are left to mark their sites. Apparently the red colour, in contrast with the grey powder obtained when a portion of the interior

FIG. 1.—The Nest of the Black-Mound Termite. It is about two feet high and two feet across at the base and may be from twenty-five to fifty years old.

of a mound is burned in the laboratory, is due to the organic matter from the incinerated insects.

Although it is densely crowded, the inside of the termitary is always spotlessly clean and contains no food or refuse. In this city of endless night the inhabitants cast their skin six or seven times as they grow up and the narrow corridors would soon be choked with these empty husks if they were not disposed of in some way or other. The termites get rid of them by eating them. Nothing is wasted in this frugal domain and the cast-off skins are made to serve as food. It is the same with their method of disposing of the dead. A cemetery is not needed inside the crowded fortress because the dead are eaten by the living.

Ventilation inside the mound is very poor indeed as it is entirely closed and air can diffuse but slowly through the tiny pores in the dense walls. The inhabitants live in a perpetual fug and they have become so accustomed to it that they dislike fresh air and avoid it if they can. It is quite easy to obtain a sample of air from the interior of the mound and to test it for its carbon dioxide content. A hole is bored into the mound with an ordinary brace and bit, about half an inch in diameter and deep enough to reach the centre of the termitary. Then a glass tube is pushed into the hole and sealed in position with clay and left there for twelve hours or so, until the air in the tube has acquired the same composition as that in the mound. The tube is then withdrawn and the amount of carbon dioxide determined by standing it mouth downwards in a vessel of strong caustic potash. The solution of caustic potash absorbs the carbon dioxide and rises in the tube and it is a simple matter to calculate the percentage of carbon dioxide that was present in the air. When this is done, four to five per cent. of carbon dioxide is usually found to be present in the air inside a mound. In such an atmosphere a man would go blue in the face and gasp for breath, but the termites thrive in it. Furthermore, in midsummer, when breeding is going on apace and the termitary is thronged with active insects, the percentage of carbon dioxide may rise to as high as fifteen per cent., an atmosphere in which a man would quickly lose consciousness.

The temperature inside the mound can also be ascertained by boring holes and inserting thermometers in them. When the thermometers are removed and examined it is found that the range of temperature inside the termitary is much less than that of the surrounding air. This is to be expected, because the cellular structure acts as an air blanket. On a hot summer's afternoon, when the outside wall of the mound is heated by the direct rays of the sun and it is too hot to bear the hand upon it, the temperature in the centre of the nest is only about thirty degrees Centigrade. On a cold winter's day the temperature inside the nest may be nine or ten degrees warmer than the outside air.

A word of warning may not be out of place here. Any reader who wishes to test the temperature inside a termitary should not leave his thermometers undisturbed in the wall of the mound for any length of time because, if he does this, he will find the thermometers stuck so fast that they cannot be removed without breaking. The termites do this to any foreign object in their home; they fix it securely and firmly in place with their excremental cement. For this reason, any glass tubes or other apparatus inserted in a mound must be moved every day.

The termites move about in their home so as to secure for

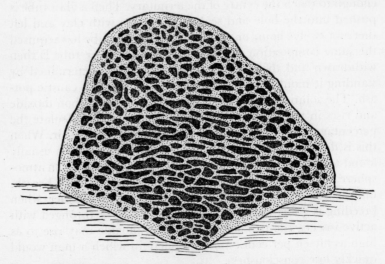

FIG. 2.—Diagram showing structure of the interior of a mound. The cells are half an inch to an inch in diameter and are connected with one another by small, circular openings.

themselves the optimum temperature conditions. On a hot afternoon the outer cells of the mound are empty and all the inhabitants are crowded into the lower part of the nest, where it is cooler. During the winter, on the other hand, they will congregate in the superficial cells on a sunny day for the sake of the warmth. If the weather grows very cold they retreat right down into the lowest part of the nest. These little creatures dislike fresh air, draughts, and rapid changes of temperature far more than the fussiest of human valetudinarians.

Because the ventilation is so bad and the small chambers are so crowded, the atmosphere inside the mound is very humid. In fact, termites die very quickly if they are placed in a dry atmosphere. As they need humid air and as they live in warm regions where the rainfall is often low, it has been suggested that termites must burrow deep down into the earth, perhaps for a hundred feet or more, in order to get at underground sources of water. This is not the case with the black-mound termite. Although the summer months at the Cape are hot and dry, with the fierce south-east wind often blowing for days at a time from a cloudless sky, the termites have little difficulty in maintaining a humid atmosphere inside their home. They feed only on moist food and are particularly active after rain and in this way they get all the water they need. Inside the termitary the loss of water vapour is very slight because of the lack of ventilation and the air inside the small cells is always humid, no matter what the weather is like outside.

As the population increases, the mound must be enlarged from time to time to accommodate the growing numbers. These extensions to the premises are always made in the spring, in August and September, and at no other time of the year. At this season the queen is not laying and there are no young in the nest to be cared for, consequently the workers have more time for building. Also the winter rains have thoroughly soaked the outer wall of the mound and it is softer than at other times of the year. All the activities of the colony are strictly controlled and regulated, but how and by whom or by what we have no idea. This interesting problem is discussed fully in a later chapter and it must suffice to say here that the building extensions are always carried out during a fortnight or so in early spring, when there is little other work going on, and all the colonies at the Cape perform the work at about the same time.

The workers do not venture out on to the exterior of the mound in order to enlarge it. They dare not do this because they would be quickly attacked and carried off by ants. Theirs is a difficult problem and it will help us to understand it if we imagine a man in the same position, wishing to add a new wing to his house but not daring to go outside because of numerous foes lurking there, ready to fall upon him and kill him. In such a dilemma, the man might build his extension by knocking a small hole in the wall and putting his arms through this opening

and cementing a few bricks in place. Then he could knock
another hole near the first and add a few more bricks, and so he
could go on until he had built a bulge on the outside of the wall,
without once exposing himself to his enemies. After this he could
break through into the bulge and then add another outside this,
and so on until he had the addition he wanted—a difficult and
laborious way of doing things, but one forced upon him by
circumstances.

This is exactly what the termites do. They make tiny holes
close together in the outer wall of the mound where the extension is to be built, holes just big enough for them to put their
heads through. They thrust sand particles moistened with their
rapid-hardening cement through these holes and these stick

Fig. 3.—The manner in which termites build additional accommodation. They work under cover the whole time for fear of their
age-long foes, the true ants.

together and form a moist patch on the outside of the mound.
As soon as this is firm enough the insects go into the bulge and
make holes in it and add more sand grains on the outside. So it
goes on, thousands of them working together until a layer half
an inch thick or more is added over as large an area of the
mound as is considered necessary.

If, whilst the building operations are going on, a portion of the
moist, crumbly patch is swept away, numerous workers will be
found just beneath it, most of them with sticky grains of sand
in their jaws. Among them are many soldiers, with waving
antennæ and wide-open jaws, on guard all the time amid the
workers and ready to fight to the death any intruders that might
break into the weak, newly-constructed portion of the mound.
As quickly as possible the workers add to the inside of the bulge
until it is quite solid and then they hollow out the new cells they

require in the old wall just beneath the new. In this way they add to their home year by year, always in the early spring, after the heavy rains are over and the weather is getting warmer. Only after the extra accommodation has been built does the queen start to lay and more young are reared.

A walk over the veld at this time of the year and an examination of the mounds whilst the extensions are being built will show whether the colonies are in a flourishing condition or not. A colony in a healthy state will add a layer about an inch thick over the greater part of the exterior of the nest, whilst a weak colony will add only small patches here and there on the upper part of the mound. Termitaries with no extensions at all in the spring have either reached the limit of their growth or they are dwindling and dying out for some reason or other.

The only building operations that are carried out at any other time of the year consist of essential repairs. If a portion of a mound is broken away the inhabitants do not attempt to replace it until the time for major extensions arrives in the following spring. But they must and they do take immediate steps to close up the small openings that lead to the interior of the nest and that might give access to enemies. If you sit down beside a termitary after you have made a breach in the wall you can, with a little patience, see the insects at work, closing with feverish haste the small circular holes that lead to the interior. This is a matter of life and death for them because any ants in the vicinity would pour in through the openings as soon as they discovered them.

Whilst the soldiers run about over the broken part of the mound, ready to seize any enemy in a bull-dog grip, the workers examine the extent of the damage by the delicate sense of touch—you must remember that they are all stone blind. They neglect entirely the gaping walls of the broken cells and attend only to the small openings that lead to the interior. Without exposing their bodies, the heads of a number of workers appear at each of these holes, each carrying in its jaws a sand grain moistened with saliva and gut-content. As fast as they can, each one deposits its burden at the edge of the hole and then retires at once to make room for a newcomer. In this way the small holes are blocked up in a matter of seconds and any workers or soldiers that may be running about on the outside are shut out and left to their fate. The safety of the community demands this sacrifice.

Whilst the holes are being closed ants may appear on the scene. Frequently certain species of ants make their homes in the walls of the mounds or just beneath them and it is surprising how quickly they become aware of the presence of termites in the open air. Probably they learn this by the sense of smell, but certain it is that they are soon on the spot and they carry off any termites they can capture, to tear them to pieces for food. Frequently an ant will arrive at a hole just as a worker is placing a sand grain in position and the ant will grab the termite and drag it away, whilst the place of the abducted worker is immediately filled by another, and the breathless work goes on as though nothing had happened. Even though dozens of workers are carried away to their death, the others carry on until all the holes are blocked and the fortress is secure once more. It may happen that those ruthless hunters, the driver ants (*Dorylus* species) that are so common in many parts of Africa, may be burrowing nearby and if they succeed in gaining access to the mound then the struggle is fierce and bitter indeed and it generally ends in the total destruction of the colony. After you have witnessed a scene like this you will have no difficulty in understanding why all termites are doomed to live in perpetual darkness in their stout-walled homes. It is the price they have to pay for survival.

As will be shown later, in the chapter dealing with kings and queens, a termite colony should be able to carry on indefinitely, but this does not happen. In the case of the black-mound termite the life of a colony is limited to half a century or less. A full-sized mound, about two feet high by two feet across at the base, takes some twenty-five to thirty years to reach this size, but it is difficult to determine how long it may go on after this, as there are no building extensions in subsequent years and it does not increase in size.

It is easy enough to measure the annual growth of a mound. I simply bought a few pounds of six-inch nails and stuck a few of these into each of a number of mounds of various sizes on the veld (see Plate II). The points of the nails were only driven in an inch deep, so that five inches projected from the surface of the mounds and they looked something like queer porcupines undergoing a severe moult. Fortunately the mountain slopes where these mounds are found are not frequented by picnickers or hikers, therefore the nails attracted no attention and were not interfered with. The nails got buried deeper and deeper year by year as the termites built their homes outwards, and all I had to do was to measure from time to time the length of the projecting nails in order to ascertain the growth of the termitaries (Plate IIa). By this simple method I found that a vigorous colony adds a layer about an inch thick over the greater part of the surface in one year, all this being done during the brief period in spring.

The food supply seems to be the major factor that limits the growth. After it reaches a certain size a colony has difficulty in securing enough food for its teeming population and it ceases to increase in numbers and the mound stops growing. This all-important food problem is dealt with fully in a later chapter, so there is no need to say more about it here. When a colony has reached its maximum size it may remain stationary for some years and then, for some reason or other, the numbers begin to dwindle until finally the colony dies out altogether. Sometimes, when a large mound is broken open on the veld it is found to be empty, or to have only a few inhabitants lingering on in cells near the base. Other mounds may be seen that are grey instead of black and that have furrows washed in them by the rain; these are dead termitaries that are being weathered away. These dark fortresses, then, are by no means everlasting. It is estimated that fifty years is about their limit of existence and that thirty years of life is a good average. This is true only of the black-mound termite; the large termitaries of some of the Central African species may last much longer.

There are very few authentic records bearing on the age of termitaries. One of the best known of these is that given by the Australian entomologist, G. F. Hill, in his *Termites from the Australian Region*, published in 1942. He says: 'In 1872 the top of a rather large nest of *Eutermes triodiæ* was broken off so that it would not engage the telegraph wires above it; when examined by me in 1913, and again in 1935, the broken part had not been rebuilt, but the remainder of the structure was in good repair and its population apparently normal.' The mound when first seen was about fourteen feet high so it must have been fairly old then and the colony survived for more than sixty years after this; but the fact that there were no building additions during this period shows that it had reached its maximum size. No secondary or tertiary kings or queens have ever been found in the nests of the species mentioned, *Eutermes triodiæ*, therefore it would seem that the original pair, the founders of the colony, can survive for

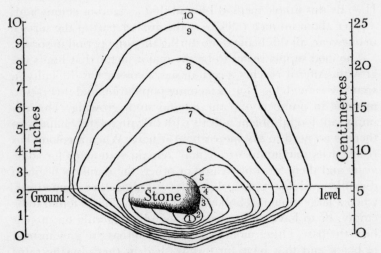

FIG. 4.—Diagram showing the annual increase in size of a normal mound. The growth is very slow at first but it increases after four or five years, and then it stops altogether after about twenty-five years.

something like three-quarters of a century. There is another possibility, however, and that is that the original colony died out and the empty mound was reinfested later. This happens occasionally with the black-mound termite.

The foundation of new colonies of the black-mound termite is fully described in a later chapter, but it may be pointed out here that the growth is very slow during the first two years of a colony's existence. By the end of the first year it consists only of a single cell about half an inch in diameter, containing the young king and queen and some half a dozen stunted workers. This cell is situated two or three inches below the surface of the ground, generally beneath a stone or dead stump of a tree or bush. At the end of the second year the colony consists of four or five cells, with about two hundred inhabitants, and it is still completely hidden beneath the soil. After this the growth is more rapid and the small mound begins to appear at the surface of the ground in the fourth or fifth year as a slight, rounded, dark-coloured protuberance. By the time it is ten years old the mound is seven or eight inches high and has the characteristic shape and contains several thousand inhabitants.

The rate of growth depends mainly on the vigour of the queen and on the food supply. If the queen is healthy and lays a large number of eggs, and if plenty of food is coming in to feed the increasing population, then the growth of the mound is rapid, but there may be checks in the annual increase through the death of the queen or through long droughts and consequent lack of food. As a general rule, it may be said that a mound two feet high is about twenty-five years old, but a smaller mound than this may be older because the colony has suffered setbacks.

## Chapter Three

## THE TEEMING THRONG

WHEN a mound is broken open the inhabitants are thrown into wild confusion, just as human beings would be if their city were overwhelmed by an earthquake. Exposed to the open air and the light, the termites are very agitated and they try to hide themselves as quickly as possible. There are several thousands of them in a large termitary and it is difficult to learn much about them as they run in a state of panic amid the ruins of their home.

What one sees when a mound is broken open depends upon the time of the year. During the winter only adults are present in the nest and the great majority of these are workers, sterile males and females about one-fifth of an inch long, with round white heads and soft abdomens dark grey or black. About five per cent. of the inhabitants are soldiers, which are also sterile males and females, with large, yellow heads and powerful, curved jaws; they are the same size as the workers. All these are quite blind, with no trace of eyes on their heads or wings on their backs (Plate III).

An important difference between termites and ants, bees and wasps should be noted here. In the beehive and ants' nest there are only female workers and soldiers; these are communities of females run by females for females; males only appear in the nests at intervals and they die or are killed off soon after the mating flight. In the termitary, on the other hand, males and females are always present in about equal numbers, although the great majority of them are never allowed to grow up properly and they are incapable of reproducing their kind.

If you are lucky, and if you hunt carefully, you may find the king and the queen. There is no special royal cell in the black-mound termites' nest, as there is in the homes of the fungus-growing termites. Despite her bulky abdomen, the queen of the black-mound termite can creep about slowly and she moves from cell to cell inside the nest, seeking the conditions that suit her best. If the opening connecting two cells is too small for her to pass through, the workers will enlarge it temporarily to give her passage. She is half to three-quarters of an inch in length, depending on her age, for, unlike her large family, she continues to increase in size after she has become adult. Most of her bulk

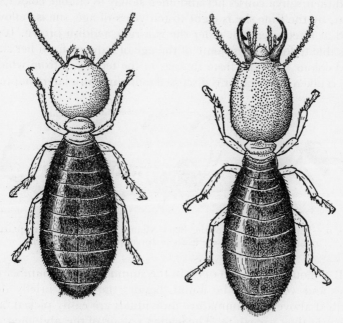

FIG. 5.—The Black-Mound Termite. Adult worker on the left, adult soldier on the right. They are sterile males and females, about one-fifth of an inch long and quite blind.

is made up of her sausage-shaped abdomen, bloated with eggs and fat. Her thorax is small and bears on it the stumps of the two pairs of wings she used on her brief wedding flight. On her head she has a pair of compound eyes and two simple eyes, eyes that she uses only once in her life, also on that brief nuptial excursion into the open air. The king is dark brown and only about a quarter of an inch long, a nervous little fellow who spends nearly all his time close beside his mate and who tries to hide himself under her huge abdomen if he is alarmed. He also has

stumps of wings on his back and compound and simple eyes on
his head (Plate IV).

If the queen is not more than four or five years of age—that is
to say, if she is taken from a small mound—her abdomen is white
and she is only about half an inch long. During her life, however, her sons and daughters, the workers, lick her constantly
and their saliva causes her abdomen slowly to change colour, so
that, by the time she is eight to ten years of age, she is yellow,
and at fifteen years or older she is a rich, reddish brown. It is
possible to form an estimate of the age of a queen from her size
and colour, and also from the size of the termitary from which
she is taken; this matter is discussed more fully in a later chapter.

FIG. 6.—King and Queen of the Black-Mound Termite. He is a quarter
of an inch long and she is about three-quarters of an inch.

If a mound is broken open in the summer a large number of
eggs and young will be found, besides the adults briefly described above. The immature individuals are easily picked out
because they are white. The leaden colour of the abdomen of
the adult worker and soldier is due to the coarse food in the alimentary canal showing through the translucent wall of the body.
The young, however, are fed on predigested food by the adult
workers and this is colourless (Plates III and V).

At midsummer, in January, in a flourishing colony, larger
individuals may be present, in addition to those already mentioned. These also are white, because they are fed like the other
immature members of the community, and they have four white
wing-pads on their backs and small eyes on their heads (Plate
VIa). Apart from the king and queen, they are the only individuals in the colony with eyes. They are the only ones in the
nest that are being allowed to develop fully into mature males

and females; they are the young princes and princesses being reared in readiness for the great event of the year, the nuptial flight that is to take place in the autumn; they are the future kings and queens, the founders of new colonies if they survive long enough. In February and March they turn into winged adults, with four smoky wings, and they are kept prisoners in the nest until the time arrives for the mating exodus (Plate VIb).

Entomologists use two words in speaking of young insects; they call them larvæ and nymphs. Usually the term *larva* is applied to an immature insect that differs markedly from the adult, for example, a caterpillar, whilst the word *nymph* is used when speaking of a young insect that resembles the adult, for example, a young plant bug or louse. In dealing with termites it is convenient to use both these terms and to call all the young that have no trace of wings on their backs *larvæ*, and to speak of those with wing-pads as *nymphs*. The individuals described in the previous paragraph, then, are nymphs, and as they have long wing-pads and are white they may be called long-winged white nymphs.

In addition to these, other nymphs may be found in some termitaries at any time of the year. They have short wing-pads and are grey in colour because they are fed on coarser food, and they may be spoken of as short-winged grey nymphs (Plate VIIa). They are the same size as the long-winged white nymphs (Plate VIa). These two types of nymphs are important and more will be said about them later on, but in the meantime it should be noted that the long-winged nymphs are to be found only at midsummer and only in flourishing colonies, whereas the short-winged nymphs, usually much less numerous, may be present in comparatively small colonies and at any season. Both may often be found together in a colony.

It is impossible to form a reliable estimate of the number of inhabitants in a mound by just watching the insects milling around amid their broken home. Yet for certain experiments it is necessary to know their approximate number. The easiest way to count them with any approach to accuracy is to carry the mound into the laboratory and there to break it up and shake the termites out on to a sheet of glass. By placing a shallow cardboard box next to the glass, with small holes in the side and a wad of damp cotton wool to create a humid atmosphere, the insects can be induced to creep into the box to find darkness and shelter. In this way they are readily separated from the debris of their nest. Then 500 of them are picked up at random from the throng and carefully weighed in a delicate balance. They are so small and soft bodied that they are difficult to handle but they can be picked up quickly and without injury by means of a piece of apparatus called an aspirator, or suction bottle.

The aspirator consists of a small glass bottle with two tubes of plastic or glass inserted through the cork as shown in the

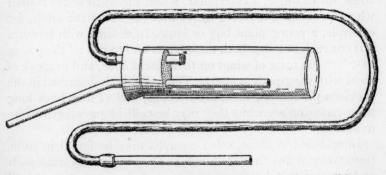

Fig. 7.—An Aspirator, or Suction Bottle. Termites and other small insects can be picked up quickly and without injury by means of this simple piece of apparatus. The investigator sucks air through the mouthpiece attached to the rubber tubing whilst aiming the tube that projects from the bottle at the insects. The insects are drawn into the bottle by the current of air.

illustration. The investigator holds the end of the tube that projects from the cork near the insects and then sucks air through the mouthpiece attached to the rubber tubing, and they are drawn into the bottle by the current of air. Any required number can be picked up in this way without harming them.

Half a dozen lots of 500 adult soldiers and workers were picked up by means of an aspirator and carefully weighed, and their average weight was found to be 1·173 grammes. This was a tedious business, but it was necessary to get this basic figure as accurate as possible because it was used in all future calculations. Then a large number of termites were dumped into a graduated cylinder until their volume measured twenty cubic

PLATE III

(*a*) Some of the inhabitants of the mound

Adult workers, secondary kings and queens, and short-winged grey nymphs may be seen in the photograph. The workers are about one-fifth of an inch long.

(*b*) Adult workers and immature stages

The young are white because they are fed on colourless food

PLATE IV

(*a*) Primary king and queen of the black-mound termite
They are five or six years old and she is about half-an-inch long

(*b*) An old primary queen of the black-mound termite
She is more than fifteen years old, about three-quarters of an inch long
and reddish brown in colour

centimetres. It was found that these weighed 13·405 grammes, and it was now a simple sum in arithmetic to ascertain that twenty cubic centimetres contained some 5,714 termites. After this, all that had to be done in order to learn the approximate number of inhabitants in any mound was to break it up and measure the volume of the termites. By this method it was found that a small mound, five inches high and six inches across at the base contained between 10,500 and 11,000 insects. The greatest number found was 40,000, in a mound twelve inches high and fifteen inches across. The largest mound broken up, which was two feet high by two feet across, contained only 30,000 inhabitants. This census was carried out in the winter, when there were only adults present in the nests. The termites taken from these mounds were used in the flower-pot experiments described later in this book.

These numbers are much lower than the estimates given by other entomologists working with other species of termites in various parts of the world. In some cases the figures quoted run into millions and they may be true for certain tropical species that live in very large termitaries, but I do not think the colonies of the black-mound termite ever exceed 50,000 or so. In any case, the figures I give are remarkable enough when it is remembered that they represent the progeny of one mother and father in each case. The 40,000 mentioned in the previous paragraph was the family of a primary queen about fifteen years old, and there is no means of telling how many had died before the count was made or how many she might have gone on producing if her home had not been broken up.

*Chapter Four*

# SLAVES OF THE STATE

ABOUT ninety-five per cent. of the inhabitants of a termitary are workers. These are males and females that have not developed fully and their sexual organs are vestigial and useless. As their sex organs do not function, the workers are denied the privilege of parenthood and they know nothing of the distractions of sex. This is the drastic method of population control that has been followed by all social insects. If the teeming throng in the beehive, ants' nest or termite mound were all to produce offspring in the usual way, then their numbers would quickly outgrow the food supply. Consequently the right of parenthood is denied to all but the select few we call kings and queens. All the other members of the colony are sterile and can devote all their time and attention to ceaseless labour for the good of the community as a whole.

The adult worker of the black-mound termite is only about five millimetres, or one-fifth of an inch in length. All termites are small insects, the largest of them being less than an inch in length and the smallest being only about one-eighth of an inch; the queens are an exception, those of certain tropical species reaching a length of four inches, but the workers and soldiers never attain anything like this size. The black-mound termite worker has a large round white head, a narrow white thorax and a soft abdomen that is dark grey in colour and more or less mottled by the patches of fatty tissue showing through the translucent skin. The body appears to be smooth and shiny, but under the microscope, numerous hairs, or setæ, as they should be called, can be seen scattered over the antennæ, legs, thorax and abdomen; even the smooth head is sparsely coated with them. These are delicate organs of touch. Being blind, the worker has to rely mainly on its sense of smell and touch for information about its surroundings.

In the dark interior of their homes day and night mean

nothing to the termites. They are active throughout the twenty-four hours of the day, but more so at night than by day. They do have periods of rest, however. In my observation nests, which are described in the last chapter, I see groups of them standing motionless in some of the cells, with their heads close together like a lot of sheep, and they may remain like this for a few hours, whilst their companions bustle around them.

The antennæ of the workers are situated low down on the head and are white and consist of thirteen or fourteen segments.

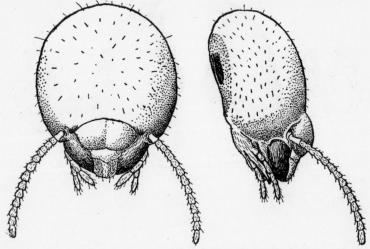

Fig. 8.—Head of Adult Worker of the Black-Mound Termite. Front view on left, side view on right.

It is not possible to be sure of the number of joints in the antennæ in all cases because the third segment, counting from the head, subdivides as the termite grows and these subdivisions are often indistinct. The newly-hatched termite has only nine or ten segments in its antennæ and the number increases as it grows by the division of the third segment, until there are thirteen or fourteen in the adult. There are numerous sensory pores, pits and setæ on the antennæ and they are delicate organs of smell and touch and they may have other functions about which we know nothing.

The only tools by means of which the worker termite carries out its varied tasks are its mouthparts. It uses these in building the home, tunnelling through the soil, protecting itself, collecting food, caring for the eggs and young, grooming its companions, and so on. The jaws are large and strong and armed with toothlike projections. These "teeth" get worn down and blunted in older workers because of the hard usage they get, and they enable one to form some estimate of the age of a worker. Workers that have recently assumed the adult state have sharp points on their mandibles, whereas older ones have these teeth worn down and rounded.

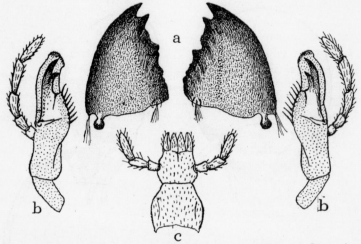

Fig. 9.—Mouthparts of the Adult Worker: (*a*) mandibles, or first pair of jaws, (*b*) maxillæ, or second pair of jaws, (*c*) labium, or third pair of jaws fused together.

Under the high power of the microscope tiny pores can be seen on the mandibles, connected with nerves, and it would seem that, hard though they are, they are sensitive implements; it might even be that, on occasion, the workers suffer from "toothache." Behind the mandibles are the second pair of jaws, or maxillæ. These are complex organs and consist each of a double lobe with a five-jointed feeler, or maxillary palp. The lower lobe is membranous and covers the upper one like a hood. Both are well supplied with sensory setæ and pits, and the upper lobe, or lacinia, looks like a double curved claw. The lower lobe, or galea, is roughened at the tip and may serve as a brush for grooming and cleaning, whilst there is a row of stiff bristles along the inner edge of each lacinia that serves as a comb. The workers are constantly licking their companions and it seems that the maxillæ are the principal toilet implements.

Below the maxillæ is the lower lip, or labium, which is really a third pair of jaws fused together. It has four lobes in front and bears a pair of three-jointed feelers, the labial palps. In addition to these mouthparts, there is the upper lip, or labrum, that hangs down from the front of the head and covers the mandibles. Although they are very simple in structure when compared with the highly modified mouthparts of flies and bees, they are nevertheless complex and efficient organs. They are very similar indeed to the mouthparts of a cockroach.

The legs are white and rather short and are also armed with numerous setæ. The feet, or tarsi, are four-jointed, the first three being small and indistinctly separated, with a larger end joint that bears a pair of claws. There are no sticky pads on the feet, such as are found in the house-fly and other insects, therefore a termite cannot crawl up a window-pane and it can only walk over a smooth surface with difficulty. This leads to an unfortunate habit when they are kept under glass in an observation nest. They coat the underside of the glass with their excrement and this is black and obscures the view and means that the glass must be removed from time to time for cleaning. At first I thought they did this to exclude the light, but they do it just the same when the glass is kept covered, and they also coat the inside of the glass tubes used in the feeding experiments (see page 127) in the same way. They do it to create a non-skid surface for ease of walking. It has been reported that the excreta of termites is corrosive and that they will even corrode glass, but this is not the case with the black-mound termite; the substance is easily washed off and leaves no mark.

Termites are slow-moving insects and their speed is regulated by the temperature; they move faster on a warm day than when the weather is cold. If they are alarmed in any way they can speed up their movements temporarily, but when left undisturbed they move at a uniform speed. In order to test accurately the relationship between speed and temperature I devised the piece of apparatus shown in the diagram and this gave some interesting results.

A piece of sheet cork, eighteen inches by three inches, had a cell one inch in diameter punched at each end, and a straight groove, an eighth of an inch deep and the same width, was cut to connect the two. A wider, deeper groove was cut in the cork parallel with the first and large enough to accommodate a thermometer. A shallow tray of sheet copper was made just large enough to take the piece of cork. The shallow groove that formed the runway between the cells had a scale in centimetres marked along it so that the termites could be timed as they ran to and fro in it. Finally a strip of glass covered the whole.

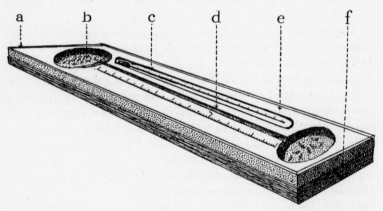

FIG. 10.—The Speedway. Apparatus for determining the relationship between speed and temperature: (*a*) glass cover, (*b*) cell containing termites, (*c*) thermometer, (*d*) runway connecting the two cells, (*e*) sheet cork, (*f*) sheet copper base.

About fifty adult workers were placed in one of the cells and the "speedway" was put in a shadowy corner of the laboratory and the termites soon settled down and learned to make their way from one cell to the other along the groove. Watching them, one was struck by the uniformity of their speed. Traffic control is not necessary in the termite community because there is no speeding and no overtaking. A worker that starts out along the groove at, say, a distance of one centimetre behind another, maintains this distance throughout the course. This must be a very useful characteristic when they are proceeding along their narrow tunnels underground; although these cramped thoroughfares are crowded, there are no traffic jams because all move at precisely the same speed.

By timing the termites as they moved along the runway on cold, mild and warm days their speeds at temperatures between 10 and 30 degrees Centigrade were ascertained. Lower temperatures were obtained by placing the whole apparatus in the refrigerator and higher temperatures by warming the copper base gently over a spirit lamp. Even under optimum conditions, termites are certainly not speedy insects. The following table gives a summary of some results obtained at different times of the year, fifty adults being timed on each occasion.

*Speed and Temperature*

| Temp. | Time taken in seconds to cover fifty centimetres | | | Approx. speed in centimetres per minute | Approx. speed in yards per hour |
|---|---|---|---|---|---|
| | Min. | Max. | Average | | |
| 12° C. | 164 | 169 | 167 | 18 | 11·8 |
| 19° C. | 102 | 105 | 103 | 29 | 19·0 |
| 23° C. | 82 | 87 | 84 | 36 | 23·5 |
| 30° C. | 61 | 67 | 64 | 47 | 30·7 |

It will be noticed that the speed in centimetres per minute is approximately fifty per cent. higher than the number of degrees Centigrade, whilst in yards per hour it is, curiously enough, roughly equal to the number of degrees Centigrade—10 yards per hour at 10 degrees, 20 yards per hour at 20 degrees, and 30 yards per hour at 30 degrees. As the temperature approaches 40 degrees the insects show signs of distress and they move erratically and they are killed after a few minutes' exposure to 41 degrees—but this may be due to loss of moisture as much as to the heat. When placed in the refrigerator they are rendered motionless by a temperature of 4 degrees Centigrade, but they quickly recover when returned to room temperature, even after being kept in the refrigerator for twelve hours or longer. They recover much more slowly after an hour's exposure to —9 degrees Centigrade, the temperature of the small chamber in which ice-cubes are made, and they are killed if kept for more than twelve hours in this chamber.

Thus the speed of movement is strictly controlled by the temperature, and it is clear from the above results that termites cannot survive in a cold country, because they would be rendered helpless and motionless for weeks or months at a time during the winter, when the temperature dropped to near freezing point or lower. Ants also move at a speed that is related to the temperature, but they are much faster and more erratic than termites. For example, Dr. H. Shapley, the American astronomer, reported some years ago the results of experiments he carried out with the ant, *Liometopum apiculatum*. He found that this ant moves at an average speed of 36 centimetres per minute at 10 degrees Centigrade, at 120 centimetres per minute at 20 degrees and 180 centimetres at 30 degrees. At the same temperatures the black-mound termite moves at approximately only 15, 30 and 45 centimetres per minute. It is, therefore, easy to understand why termites are no match for their agile, aggressive foes and why they must hide themselves in their fortress homes.

Also the slowness of their movement limits severely the distance over which termites can range when out foraging for food. On a warm day, at a temperature of 30 degrees Centigrade, they would take more than six hours to travel to a point one hundred yards from their nest and back, whilst on a cold day, at 10 degrees Centigrade, such a journey would take them twenty hours or so. It is probable, then, that these insects do not go very far from their nests in their never-ending hunt for food, and it may be their speed, or rather their lack of it, that limits the growth of a colony as much as anything else.

Although they are quite blind, termites are aware at once when they are exposed to strong light. They show this by their movements and their peculiar method of signalling alarm. If they are watched when the cover is taken off an observation nest, a number of them will be seen to start jerking their bodies to and fro in a quaint fashion. This is the method of signalling adopted by all termites. Adult workers and soldiers do it, but not the immature individuals. Even the queens do it if their abdomens are not too bulky and the kings are quite vigorous jerkers when disturbed.

It is difficult to determine what is the exact nature of this signal and how the termites, blind as they are and living in total darkness, become aware of it. No sound is made—at least, not usually, because the body of the insect is so soft and, in any case, it does not seem to strike the ground as the termite jerks itself backwards and forwards. Nevertheless, if timber that is badly infested with termites is tapped and the ear placed close to it, a rustling sound can be heard and it is assumed that this is caused by the jaws of the workers and soldiers striking the wood as they signal alarm. Furthermore, even in the case of the black-mound termite, a faint ticking sound can be heard if a large number of them are dumped on to a sheet of glass.

A few experiments were carried out in co-operation with the engineers of the Cape Town studios of the South African Broadcasting Corporation, in which a delicate ribbon microphone, an amplifier and filters were used in an attempt to magnify and identify the sound. When the termites were allowed to walk on the microphone a sound similar to that made when stiff paper is crumpled or when rice grains are dropped on a board was heard, but it was impossible to determine whether the jerking movement produced a distinct sound of its own or not. Unfortunately, these experiments had to be discontinued owing to stress of other work, but further investigations along these lines might lead to some interesting results.

Even though a sound is made by their peculiar movement, it is doubtful whether the termites can hear it because, as far as we know, they have no ears. Like many other insects, they have what are called chordotonal organs in their legs that may serve as very simple ears, capable of detecting vibrations, in the air and in the soil. Also the pair of short feelers on the hind end of the body, called cerci, and the numerous sensitive hairs on the body and limbs may be capable of detecting changes in pressure in the surrounding atmosphere. Although we cannot say precisely what is the nature of the signal sent out by the jerking termites, it is obvious that the others are quickly aware of it, because the alarm spreads rapidly among them when they are disturbed. In particular, soldiers come hurrying towards the spot where the signal is being given.

The termites in my nests are not disturbed by loud noises quite close to them, but I found by accident that they are thrown into a state of panic if I rub a damp finger over the glass cover of a nest and produce a squeaking sound. Immediately they begin to run about and signal furiously, but I think it is the vibrations in the substratum they detect, and not the sound conveyed through the air. Nevertheless, taps on the side of the nest do not disturb them nearly as much as the shrill squeaking of the glass.

Although they are without eyes, termites can detect differences in the nature of the light that reaches them. This can be shown by placing a piece of blue glass over one half of a nest and a piece of red glass over the other half. When a nest so covered is exposed to strong light the insects make their way under the red glass, although to the human eye the light there is brighter than that under the blue glass. If the two pieces of glass are interchanged, the termites make their way into the cells under the red glass once more and desert the cells in the blue light. If an observation nest with colourless glass cover is examined by the red or yellow light of a lamp such as photographers use in their dark rooms, then the insects do not show any signs of disturbance but proceed about their business as though in total darkness. If they are kept in a dimly lighted corner of the laboratory, where the direct rays of the sun never reach them, they learn to disregard the moderate light and run about freely under the glass, but they signal quickly enough if a bright light is brought near them.

The manner in which termites seek out a humid atmosphere can be shown if some calcium chloride is placed in a cell on one side of a nest and some wet cotton wool in a cell on the other side. Moist and dry conditions inside the nest are so created; the calcium chloride absorbs water vapour, whilst the damp cotton wool gives it off. It will be found that the termites crowd into the cells as close as possible to the cotton wool, whilst the dry part of the nest is quite deserted. If the dry side of the nest is covered so that it is in the dark and the damp side is left exposed to the light, the insects will overcome their dislike of the light and will pack into the damp cells because they cannot tolerate a dry atmosphere.

*Chapter Five*

# GUARDIANS OF THE CITADEL

ABOUT five per cent. of the inhabitants of a mound are soldiers, and these can easily be recognised by the shape of the head and jaws. Whereas the head of a worker is round and white and armed with short, broad mandibles, the head of a soldier is oval, yellow, and the mandibles are slender,

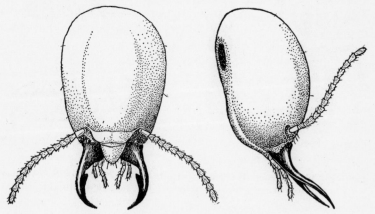

FIG. 11.—Head of a Soldier. Front view on left, side view on right.

curved, sharp and armed each with a prominent tooth about half-way along its length.

The soldiers, like the workers, are sterile males and females. They look very intelligent, with their large, shiny, bulging cranium, but in actual fact they are stupid creatures when compared with the workers. They cannot even feed themselves and, like the young and the king and queen, they have to be fed by the adult workers. They are, therefore, a drain upon the community and no more of them are tolerated than are considered necessary. One soldier to twenty workers seems to be about the average, but in some nests there are proportionately fewer soldiers.

The food given to adult soldiers is coarser than that fed to the young and the king and queen. If a soldier is hungry and solicits a worker for food, then the worker will turn her tail end and offer the semi-liquid contents of her rectum. It is in this way that the food passes through the alimentary canals of several individuals, until all the nourishment is extracted and only a dark-coloured liquid is left which is used as cement in building the mound or constructing the non-skid runways. As the food of

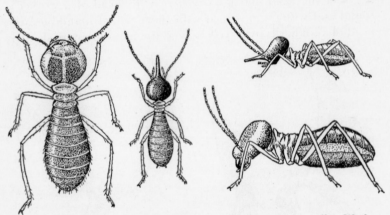

Fig. 12.—The Snouted Harvester Termite, *Trinervitermes gemellus*. Worker and soldier, viewed from above on left, side view on right.

the soldier is partially digested when he or she gets it, the colour of the abdomen is a little lighter than that of the adult worker and has a brownish tinge. When the adult workers feed one another they usually do so mouth to mouth, but the soldiers generally have to be content with nourishment from the wrong end, although occasionally one may see a soldier being fed in the more hygienic manner.

The large head of the soldier is not due to a well-developed brain. The brain is, in fact, quite small and situated close to the base of the antennæ. The greater part of the head is occupied by the large gland, called the frontal gland, which secretes a sticky, colourless fluid. This gland opens to the exterior by a pore on the front of the head, just above the base of the jaws. When a soldier grips a foe, a little of the fluid runs down on to the jaws and it has a powerful irritant effect upon the enemy. If an ant gets some of the liquid on its antennæ or body it quickly loses all interest in the fight and strives wildly to rid itself of the irritant. If it is well wetted by it, it is killed. Thus the large head and jaws of the soldier have been developed as weapons of mechanical and chemical warfare and termites were using poison sprays long before man thought of them.

The highest of all termites have brought the art of chemical warfare to a high pitch of perfection. These are the members of the subfamily *Nasutitermtinæ*, so called because they have nasute or snouted soldiers. These soldiers have no jaws, or only useless vestiges of them, but the frontal gland is well developed. The front of the soldier's head, between the antennæ, is pro-duced into a tubular snout and the poisonous secretion from the gland is squirted at the enemy through this.

There is one species of snouted harvester termite, *Trinervi-termes gemellus*, that is found about thirty miles from Cape Town, at Somerset West, and I have kept these in my laboratory for comparison with the black-mound termite. Their ways are very different. These termites come out at night and run about on the surface of the ground, hunting for the dead vegetation upon which they feed. The workers are always accompanied by a number of the small, red-headed, snouted soldiers, and there may be as many of them as there are workers on these foraging expeditions, although they do not assist in gathering the food. They run restlessly to and fro with their heads raised and, if they encounter any ants or other enemies, they shoot fine white threads of the secretion from their frontal glands at them. These threads are so slender and light that they float in the air and, if they touch an ant, that insect at once beats a hasty retreat. It is an effective means of defence and enables these insects to venture out into the open at night in order to do their harvesting. These snouted termites are also faster-moving than the black-mound termite and are therefore less vulnerable.

By cutting off the heads of a number of soldiers and crushing them on a microscope slide a fair-sized drop of the poisonous secretion can be obtained and its rapidly fatal effects on ants can be tested. If an ant is well wetted with it the insect dies almost immediately. It is remarkable that this liquid, so deadly to ants, seems to be innocuous to the termites themselves.

Nearly all the different species of termites have soldiers, individuals specially developed with highly modified heads and jaws whose sole function is to defend the community. Worker termites are all very much alike and it is not easy to distinguish one species from another when the workers only are examined, but the soldiers differ markedly in the form of their heads and jaws and they help one to recognise the different types in the field. The soldiers of the primitive harvester termites, *Hodotermitidæ*, for example, that run in the open in broad daylight, have hard, dark heads armed with compound eyes, whilst most of the other species are blind. Soldiers of some of the species that make their homes in timber have large, round heads that just fit into the narrow openings to their tunnels and effectually block them so as to keep out enemies; they are living plugs or stoppers that can be quickly put in place or removed as required. All the soldiers of the black-mound group, *Amitermes* species, have jaws similar to those in Figure 11, each armed with a tooth somewhere along its inner edge. Some of the higher termites have fantastic, over-developed jaws that are useless for feeding or biting, but which are used for striking a sideways blow at the foe. Finally there are the snouted soldiers that have concentrated on chemical warfare and have lost their jaws.

When a breach is made in the termitary of the black-mound termite the soldiers run out with wide-open jaws and waving antennæ. If a blade of grass or piece of cotton thread is brought into contact with the jaws of a soldier he will seize it in a tenacious grip and will allow his body to be torn off without releasing his hold. If, whilst he is gripping the thread, his legs are brought into contact with a small stone, he can be lifted with the stone held in his claws and he shows surprising strength for such a small, soft-bodied creature, for he can hold an object many times his own weight and size. Sometimes soldiers running over the hand of a human observer will bite, but their jaws are not strong enough to pierce the human skin. The soldiers of some of the larger species, however, such as those of the large fungus-growing termite, *Macrotermes natalensis*, can inflict a painful bite and draw blood, and investigating the interior of their nests is not a pleasant occupation, as I know from personal experience.

If ants appear on the scene the soldiers will sacrifice their lives without hesitation in defence of their home, but it is an unequal contest, in spite of the poison glands. They cannot see

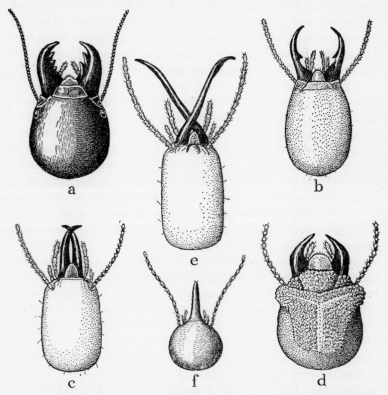

Fig. 13.—Heads of Soldiers of Different Types of Termites: (a) *Hodotermes mossambicus*, (b) *Amitermes atlanticus*, (c) *Microcerotermes malmesburyi*, (d) *Cryptotermes brevis*, (e) *Termes winifredæ*, (f) *Trinervitermes gemellus*.

their enemies and they are slow-moving when compared with the ants. It is only when a soldier blunders into a foe by chance that it can seize it in a relentless grip. Other ants may tear its body to pieces, but its jaws do not loosen their grip and the enemy loses all further interest in the struggle as soon as the secretion from the frontal gland touches it.

The soldiers make no attempt to assist the workers in blocking up the holes in the mound. They run about blindly groping for intruders and often a number of them are shut out when the workers succeed in closing all the openings leading to the interior. Such individuals are left to their fate and they invariably fall a prey to the ants. The workers will also defend themselves when attacked and, if one of them succeeds in seizing an ant in its jaws, it will hang on just as grimly as a soldier. Usually, however, they are so absorbed in their work that the ants can grab them by the thorax and carry them off with impunity.

A number of soldiers always accompany the workers when they go out foraging for food along their underground tunnels. The soldiers do not help at all in gathering the food. They stand about at intervals along the tunnels, on the alert all the time to attack any enemies that might break into the runways. Many of them gather in the cavity where the food is being collected and they mingle with the busy workers, like policemen in a milling crowd, apparently idle, but on duty all the time, ready to spring into action should an emergency arise.

Black-mound termites are nervous insects, easily alarmed. If the glass lid is removed from one of the food-chambers of an artificial nest (see page 125) then the workers at once scurry back into the nest, but the soldiers remain behind as a rearguard, running around to ascertain the cause of the disturbance (Plate IIb). This is an easy way to collect a number of soldiers for experimental purposes, because within a minute or so of the glass lid being removed, only a few dozen soldiers are left in the chamber. If there is any weak spot in the defences the soldiers gather there in numbers, as though acting under orders according to plan. For example, if the glass lid of a food-chamber is slightly raised on one side by a piece of grit under it the termites quickly become aware of this and a row of soldiers will line up there and remain there until the workers have sealed the opening with grains of sand and their intestinal cement. When a mound is broken open the soldiers are found concentrated in the outer cells and there are few deep in the interior, apparently because it is in the outer confines of the nest that danger is most likely to threaten. All the time the soldiers behave as though controlled by an iron discipline.

PLATE V

(*a*) Workers tending clusters of eggs

The eggs will not hatch if taken away from the care of the workers

(*b*) A young primary queen of the black-mound termite

White mites, *Termitacarus cuneiformis*, can be seen on the head of the queen and two of her attendants

PLATE VI

(a) Long-winged white nymphs

They are a quarter of an inch long and are only found in the nests at
mid-summer

(b) Winged termite and long-winged white nymph

The change from the latter to the former takes place in a few hours.
Winged termites are found in the nests only in the second half of summer,
from February to April.

## Chapter Six

## POPULATION CONTROL

IN books about insects the termite queen is frequently quoted as an example of amazing fecundity. It is stated that she lays an egg a second, 86,400 eggs a day, millions a month. This is certainly not true of the queen of the black-mound termite. During the winter months at the Cape, from May to September, she does not lay at all. At this time of the year her food supply is cut down by the workers and no breeding takes place during those four or five months. When the warmer weather arrives in spring the workers pay more attention to her, feed her more generously and she begins to swell asymmetrically. A bulge appears on one side or the other of her abdomen and she commences to lay eggs.

The small, kidney-shaped white eggs, about one-fortieth of an inch long, are removed by the workers as fast as they are laid, and she may lay several hundred in two or three days (Plate Va). She shows no interest at all in her eggs but just drops them behind her, where they are licked and picked up by the workers and carried away to another part of the nest. As soon as the workers have enough eggs to deal with, they reduce her food supply once more and she stops laying, maybe for two or three weeks or even longer. If things are going well with the colony and plenty of food is coming in, they feed her up again after a rest and she lays another lot of eggs—and so it goes on throughout the summer months. But if there is a prolonged drought and the food supply is deficient, the queen is not allowed to lay any more eggs for the time being. Should the position be very bad, the workers will eat the eggs, and the young as well if need be, in order to supply the rest of the community with food.

It is practically impossible to count the number of eggs laid by the queen because the workers carry them about in little batches, stuck together by their sticky saliva, removing them day by day from one part of the nest to another. The number is

4

constantly added to or depleted as more are laid or some are eaten. The eggs swell a little, apparently due to the absorption of saliva, and they are a little bigger just before they hatch than they are when first laid. They invariably fail to hatch if they are taken from the care of the workers. No matter how carefully they are treated they die and shrivel up if removed from the nest.

All that can be said with certainty is that the queen lays several hundred eggs in a few days and then she has a rest, the duration of which is largely dependent on the amount of food that is coming in. The grim Malthusian law holds full sway in the termitary and the size of the population is strictly limited by the food supply. It seems that the workers apply the control deliberately by the amount of food they give the queen and by the destruction of surplus young. During the winter they pay comparatively little attention to the queen, but when she is laying she is constantly surrounded by a number of workers that groom her and feed her assiduously.

The number of eggs laid is also dependent on the age and size of the queen. During the first year of her life she is small, only about a quarter of an inch long and little bigger than her mate. She is black and has four stumps of the wings she used on her nuptial flight still on her back. She also has two compound eyes and two simple eyes, although she no longer needs them in the pitch-black darkness of her home, which she never leaves. During this first year as queen she lays very few eggs, not more than a dozen or so, but after this her abdomen increases in size as her ovaries develop more fully and adipose tissue is formed as the result of abundant feeding by her sons and daughters.

Her abdomen continues to increase slowly in size as she grows older until, by the time she is fifteen years old or so she is about three-quarters of an inch long. She also changes colour. Her swollen abdomen is white at first but it gradually assumes a yellow tinge and this becomes deeper until finally, by the time she has reached the age of fifteen years, it is a rich reddish-brown colour. This is due to the constant licking by the adult workers; their saliva darkens anything with which it comes in contact.

A primary queen can live for twenty years or more. I have taken such a queen, the foundress of the colony, from a mound two feet high and at least twenty years old. Another primary queen I took from a mound that I had had under observation on the veld for fifteen years, watching its rate of growth. The termitary was small at the start of this period, probably four or

Fig. 14.—The Growth of the Primary Queen: (*a*) young queen immediately after the nuptial flight, (*b*) queen three or four years old, (*c*) queen about ten years old, (*d*) queen fifteen years old or more. She slowly changes colour from white to a rich reddish brown. All drawn to the same scale.

five years old. The king is potentially as long-lived as his mate, for I found a primary king in the second of the two mounds just mentioned, but I failed to find one in the first.

Although I have kept many royal couples in my observation nests, I have never seen the act of mating. According to some authors who have studied the more primitive termites, copulation takes place at frequent intervals. The male glides under the abdomen of his mate, turns over on his back and applies the tip of his abdomen to hers, and the two remain motionless in this position for some minutes. It may be the same with *Amitermes* and it is possible that mating always takes place during the night, and that is why I have not seen it.

The queen is constantly attended by a number of workers that feed her, groom her and lick her abdomen for the sake of a fatty exudation they get from her and of which they are obviously very fond. When, for some reason or other, the queen's fertility begins to wane and she is not able to lay sufficient eggs to maintain the colony in a vigorous state, then her sons and daughters, the workers, put her to death. The adult workers gather round her in close ranks, as many as can reach her bulky abdomen, and they literally lick her to death. Day and night for several days she is completely surrounded by the motionless crowd, all with their mouthparts applied to the soft skin of her abdomen and slowly she becomes thinner and thinner until finally only the empty, shrivelled skin is left, and this may be eaten or it may be decently interred in the wall of the mound. This has happened several times in nests in my laboratory and the murder of the queen always takes place in the same way. Nothing is wasted and the killing is apparently painless, for the mother of them all makes no attempt to escape and shows no signs of distress whilst the inexorable execution is going on.

There is a widespread belief in Africa that the fate of a termite colony is sealed when the queen is destroyed and there are even commercial concerns that undertake to eradicate these insects from infested buildings by the removal and destruction of the queens. But, as will be shown in a later chapter, colonies may produce secondary and tertiary kings and queens to replace the lost primaries and they may be able to carry on as vigorously as before, therefore the finding and killing of the primary queen is no remedy at all.

As a rule, the members of a colony are bitterly hostile to all other termites, even to those of the same species. If some workers and soldiers of the black-mound termite are dumped amid a lot of workers and soldiers of the same species, but from another nest, then a merciless fight at once ensues and ends only when all the intruders have been killed. Although fierce and relentless, it is by no means a spectacular battle. There is no racing to and fro, no manœuvring for position, no agile attack and defence, no skilful thrust and parry. The blind, slow-moving insects simply blunder into one another and they distinguish friend from foe by scent and bite savagely at their enemies, attempting to disembowel them. It is no uncommon thing in one of these grim battles to see a tangled group of four or five insects, each tearing out the entrails of the one in front whilst its own abdomen is being torn to pieces.

This hostility to strangers serves a useful purpose in helping to prevent the spread of parasites and diseases from one colony to another, and it also helps to prevent overcrowding of the mounds on the veld. But the enmity does not extend to kings and queens. I find that I can exchange royal couples from one nest to another and they will be accepted. If a colony is left without a king and queen for some time and then a strange pair are introduced from another nest, the newcomers are received with what can only be described as excitement and joy by the adult workers. They gather round the pair in what seems to the human observer to be an eager crowd, jostling one another and jerking their bodies vigorously as a sign of welcome.

If a young queen is put into a nest that has an old queen she will be accepted and the two will settle down amicably together, it may even be side by side in the same cell. But the workers do not allow this state of affairs to continue. Within a day or two they seem to come to the conclusion that two queens are unnecessary and that one of them must go. Usually it is the old queen, their mother, who is eliminated and she is murdered by licking in the customary manner, whilst the new queen takes her place. It is the same if a second king is added to a nest; one of the two kings is killed and eaten after a day or so, but in this case it is impossible to tell whether it is the father of the colony or the intruder who is killed, because both are alike; a king does not change in appearance as he grows older. It is strange that the termites will not tolerate the presence of more than one pair of primary reproductives in their nests because, as will be shown later, they will accept almost any number of secondary kings and queens.

## Chapter Seven

# REARING THE YOUNG

No eggs or young are to be found in the nests of the black-mound termite during the winter because the queen does not lay at this time of the year. Brood-rearing only starts after the heavy rains are over and the weather is warming up rapidly and the major building extensions to the mounds have been completed. The workers now pay much more attention to their mother. More of them gather round her and feed and groom her and the eggs are removed as fast as they are laid. They are gathered by the workers in heaps in cells in those parts of the nest where conditions are most favourable for them, generally somewhere near the centre of the nest (Plate Va). They are licked constantly by the workers and adhere lightly to one another, held together by the sticky saliva.

Eggs removed from the nest and placed in glass tubes in a moist atmosphere under favourable temperature conditions always fail to hatch; the attention of the workers is essential for their development. It is difficult to determine exactly the length of time the eggs take to hatch because there are so many of them, they are constantly being added to as the queen lays more, or depleted as the workers eat them, and they are carried about from cell to cell. But it can be done if a few thousand workers are isolated in an observation nest (see page 120) for a week or so and are then given a batch of eggs from another nest. They accept the eggs eagerly and care for them, although they often eat the young soon after they hatch. The eggs do not change in appearance as they develop but the embryo can be seen through the translucent shell when an egg is examined under the microscope. They take from forty to forty-five days to hatch in the spring and from thirty-two to thirty-five days at midsummer.

The newly-hatched termite is about one millimetre, or one twenty-fifth of an inch, in length and it is a feeble little creature, pure white. Here you see at once one of the major differences between termites and ants. The young termite is like the adult, with antennæ, head, thorax, abdomen and legs, whereas the immature ant is a legless maggot, quite unlike the adult. The mouthparts of the young termite are soft and budlike, quite incapable of chewing hard, coarse food. Its antennæ consist of

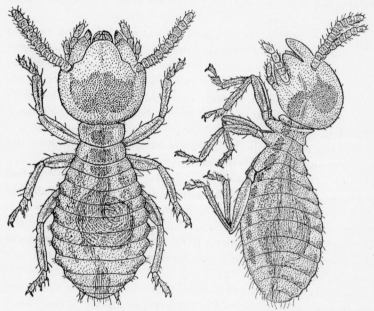

FIG. 15.—The Newly-hatched Termite. Viewed from above on left, side view on right. The little creature is white and only one twenty-fifth of an inch long. The nervous system and the gut can be seen through the translucent wall of the body.

nine or ten segments, but even at this early stage it is difficult to determine the exact number of joints because the third segment, counting from the head, is more or less distinctly sub-divided, but the divisions are often so poorly marked that it is a matter of choice whether one counts this third segment as consisting of one, two or three parts.

The young termites move about freely in the nest among the adults (Plate IIIb), but they are usually concentrated in the cells somewhere near the centre of the mound. On a summer morning, when the early rays of the sun warm the mound you may find them crowded in the superficial cells for the sake of the warmth, but later in the day the outer part of the nest becomes too hot and they retreat into the interior. The adult workers feed them with colourless, predigested food, therefore their abdomens do not become discoloured and they retain their whiteness until they begin to take coarser food when they are almost mature.

We know nothing at all about the nature of the food given to the young. Some authors state that they are fed on excrement, but I doubt very much whether this is true. In the first place, I have never seen any young being fed in this manner in my nests; only the adult workers and soldiers appear to be given this unpleasant form of nourishment. Secondly, the excrement is dark in colour and would show through the translucent wall of the young termite's body. They are fed mouth to mouth by the workers and the food is liquid. The mouthparts of the immature termite are soft and feebly chitinised and they could not deal with the coarse food of the adults. It seems highly probable that the only food they get is predigested by the adults and is mixed with salivary secretions. Just before they moult for the last time to become adults a dark discoloration appears in the abdomen for the first time and this is an indication that they are now beginning to take solid food.

Careful examination of the newly-hatched termites under the microscope reveals no visible differences among them. They all seem to be exactly alike, with large, round heads and soft, blunt mandibles, and antennæ with nine or ten segments. None has any trace of eyes or wings at this stage. Like all other insects, they cast their skin from time to time as they grow, but it is impossible to determine the number of moults of an insect such as the black-mound termite, living in densely crowded communities where the development of individuals cannot be followed.

The developmental stages between the moults are spoken of as instars; thus a newly-hatched termite is in its first instar, and after the first moult it enters upon the second instar, and so on. The moulting process takes place rapidly in the case of the black-mound termite and only rarely does one see an insect in the act of casting its skin. Probably it is helped in this difficult process by the adults and the cast-off skins are eaten as soon as they are shed. There is, however, some indication of the number of instars in the increase in the number of segments of the antennæ, from nine or ten in the newly-hatched termite to thirteen or fourteen in the adult. Assuming that a new segment is added at each moult, but remembering that it is often difficult to be sure of the exact number because of the indistinct subdivision of the third segment, we may say there are five instars in the development of the black-mound termite, with a possible sixth in some cases, characterised by 9, 10, 11, 12, 13 and 14-segmented antennæ respectively. There is a corresponding increase in body-length from one to five or six millimetres.

It is not possible to determine the length of time spent in the various instars. All that can be said is that the young grow fairly quickly and that those hatched at the end of October are mature by the end of December, a period of about two months. Eggs and young in different stages of development may be found in the nests throughout the summer months, up to the end of April, by which time, as a rule, only adults are to be seen in the mounds.

There are no visible differences between workers and soldiers until the insects are about half grown. Then, when they are probably in their third instar, young soldiers can be picked out by the shape of the head and jaws. The mandibles are still white and soft, but those of the workers are short and broad and armed with two or three small teeth, whilst those of the soldiers are longer and narrower and armed only with one tooth on the inner edge. The head of the young soldier is longer and oval when compared with the round head of the worker. In the last stage but one, in the penultimate instar, the body of the worker assumes a pale yellow shade, whilst that of the soldier retains its whiteness. The reason for this slight change of colour at this stage is unknown. The mandibles begin to harden and turn reddish-brown along their outer edges during the penultimate instar and are strong and darkly pigmented just before the insects become adults. This is when the discoloration first appears in their abdomens, showing that they are taking solid food just prior to the last moult.

Early in January a third type of young may be seen in the nests. These are half-grown individuals, similar in appearance to young workers, but they have two small triangular buds projecting from each side of the thorax (Figure 36, c and d).

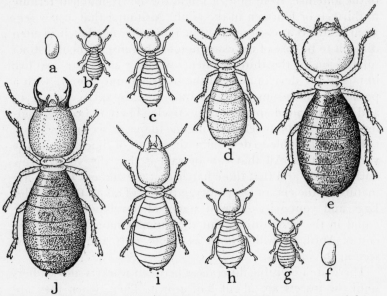

Fig. 16.—The Development of Workers and Soldiers. Top row, left to right, development of the worker; bottom row, right to left, development of the soldier. Note that there are no visible differences between a, b, and c, and f, g, and h.

These are developing wings. At the next moult they increase in size and are folded back, the first pair overlapping the second. The young with wing-buds on their backs are nymphs destined to become future kings and queens, if they survive, and their fate is dealt with in the next chapter.

## Chapter Eight

## TRAGIC NUPTIALS

IF a fair-sized mound that contains a colony in a flourishing condition is broken open at the end of January or in February large numbers of white nymphs with long wing-pads on their backs will be found among the workers and soldiers (Plate VIa). They are not found in small colonies and

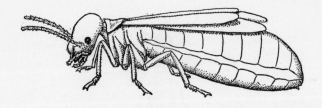

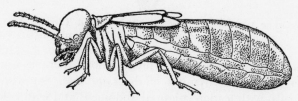

FIG. 17.—Sexual Nymphs of the Black-Mound Termite. *Above*, the long-winged white nymph that will develop into a flying termite. *Below*, the short-winged grey nymph that will never be allowed to grow up fully.

may be absent in nests that are not in a prosperous state. These are sexual individuals, young princes and princesses they might be called, that are being reared in readiness for the great event of the year, the nuptial flight in the autumn.

The wing-pads are first visible as slight, pointed protuberances on the second and third segments of the thorax of a sexual nymph in the third instar, but otherwise it is similar to a worker of the same age. The wing-pads increase in size at each succeeding moult and in the last stage but one, shown in the illustration above, they reach two-thirds along the length of the abdomen. The eyes appear at this stage and they slowly darken to black, but otherwise the nymph remains white. The mandibles are similar to those of the worker and they are strong, with sharp teeth on them, but the nymph does not take solid food; it is fed all the time by the workers. It grows bigger than the workers and reaches a length of six millimetres, or about a quarter of an inch. These long-winged white nymphs do not leave the nest at all until they are winged adults and the time arrives for them to go out on their wedding flight.

Fig. 18.—The Winged Adult of the Black-Mound Termite. It measures nearly one inch across the outspread wings.

Among the long-winged white nymphs there is usually a smaller number of nymphs of the same size, but with short wing-pads, with leaden coloured abdomens and with colourless eyes. These nymphs leave the nest and go out foraging for food with the adult workers. The darker colour of their abdomen is due to the coarse food in the alimentary canal showing through the translucent body-wall (Plate VIIa). A different destiny awaits them from that of their white brothers and sisters and this is dealt with in the next chapter.

The long-winged white nymphs moult for the last time during February and they become winged adults, fully developed males and females (Plate VIb). Immediately after this moult their wings expand and at first they are white and soft and flimsy, but they harden, stiffen and darken within twenty-four hours and the skin of the whole body turns dark brown. The winged adult, or alate as it is called, has a body about six millimetres long, with a wing-span of approximately twenty millimetres, or four-fifths of an inch. The wings are pale brown and have a few veins on them and they are carried folded one over the other along the back (Plate VIb). Besides the pair of compound eyes there are two simple eyes, or ocelli, on the head near the bases of the antennæ. This elaborate equipment of wings,

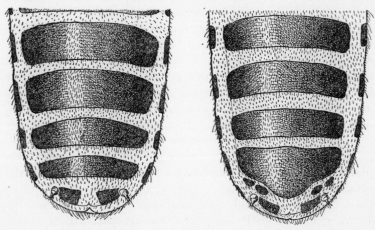

Fig. 19.—Underside of Abdomen of Flying Termite. Male on left, female on right.

eyes and hard skin is meant to serve the insect only for a few minutes once in its whole life.

The male and the female look exactly alike, but they can be distinguished one from the other if the tip of the underside of the abdomen is examined through a good hand lens. The female has a broad plate, called a sternite, followed by three smaller plates on each side of the tip of the abdomen. These are the seventh, eighth, ninth and tenth sternites respectively. The male, on the other hand, has a narrow plate, the ninth sternite, following by one small plate on each side, the tenth sternite. The abdomen of each has ten segments and the terminal segment bears a pair of short feelers, called cerci, on the ventral surface; these consist of short, two-jointed tubercles with a tuft of three or four long bristles on each, and they are found in all the different types in the nest.

The winged adults are kept prisoners in the nest for several weeks before they are allowed to leave on their nuptial flight. They spend the greater part of their time idling in the cells, crowded together and generally somewhere near the centre of the termitary. They wander about a little in search of a pleasant temperature and they may on occasion be found in the superficial cells at the top of the mound, or deep down at the base of the nest. Little attention is paid to them by the workers, except to feed and groom them from time to time. These alates make no attempt at all to assist in the work of the community. The rearing of several hundreds of them is a severe drain on the resources of the colony and that is probably why they are only found in older mounds that are in a flourishing condition. They are too expensive for small colonies to rear and that is why you never find them in small mounds only four or five years old, nor in aged termitaries that are on the way to extinction.

The nuptial flight of the black-mound termite only takes place after the autumn rains have set in at the Cape. After the ground has been thoroughly wetted, one day in late April or early May, immediately after the rain has ceased, when the weather has calmed down and the temperature is rising, generally about eleven o'clock in the morning, but it may be as late as three or four o'clock in the afternoon, the signal for the great event is given. By means which are a mystery to us, the termites are able to judge what the weather conditions are like outside their dark, sealed homes, and they time the exodus of the princes and princesses with remarkable precision, so that it occurs just when conditions outside are most favourable. Furthermore, the flight takes place simultaneously from many mounds in the vicinity, and this is important because in this way continuous inbreeding is avoided. Males and females from different nests can meet and mate.

When it is decided in some strange, mysterious way that the zero hour has arrived, the workers make a number of small holes, about one-sixteenth of an inch in diameter, close together, leading to the exterior on top of the mound, so that a small area at the apex looks something like the lid of a pepper-pot. This is

the only occasion when the workers deliberately make a breach
in the walls of their fortress home. Out of the holes come pouring
a number of workers and soldiers, closely followed by the winged
males and females, and there is a scene of great bustle and
excitement on top of the mound for a few minutes.

Not all of the alates are allowed to leave the nest on this first
flight. Some are kept back to take part in a supplementary flight
a week or so later. This is apparently a precautionary measure
in case disaster should overtake this first major flight. If you
sit beside a mound and watch whilst the males and females are
leaving you will see, after a time, that some of them are seized
by the workers and dragged back into the nest. All are eager
to take to wing, but sooner or later it is decided that enough
have gone and the rest are prevented from leaving, by force if
necessary. Who or what makes this decision we don't know, but
the whole question of authority and control in the termitary is a
fascinating one and this is discussed in a later chapter.

The bustle and excitement on top of the mound lasts only for
five or ten minutes and then, when all the winged individuals
that are to be allowed to go have flown, the workers and
soldiers go back into the nest and the small holes are plugged
from the inside. As suddenly as it started, the event is over and
all is quiet once more and the mound from the outside resumes
its lifeless aspect.

The alates are feeble fliers and many of them drop to the
ground only a few yards from their home. Some fly higher in the
air and may go fifty or sixty yards or more before settling on
some plant or on the ground. Large numbers of them are killed
during this brief excursion into the open air. Birds take a heavy
toll of them, as well as lizards, toads and other insectivores,
and predatory insects such as praying mantids, ground beetles
and ants, to say nothing of scorpions, spiders, centipedes and
others. Every creature that is an insect-eater seems to have a
great liking for the slow-moving, defenceless termites and the
slaughter among the princes and princesses is very great, only
a small percentage of them surviving the perils of their nuptial
flight.

As soon as a female termite settles, she runs a little way and
then all her wings drop off. There is a line of weakness near the

base of each wing and it is here that they break off, leaving only the small, triangular basal pieces still attached to the thorax. If you catch one of the insects and try to break off its wings you will be more likely to tear them out by the roots, yet the insect itself, with a slight movement that is too rapid to be followed by

FIG. 20.—The Nuptial Flight of the Black-Mound Termite: (1) Swarm of flying termites leaving the mound, (2) most of them flutter only a few yards before sinking to the ground, (3) the female settles and rids herself of her wings and then gives off a subtle scent to attract a male, (4) a male settles behind her and drops his wings and then the two move off, tandem fashion, with her leading the way, (5) they burrow into the ground, (6) snugly lodged in a cell underground, they settle down for their long, slow task of founding a new colony.

the eye, casts them away with ease. She shrugs her shoulders, as it were, and all her wings lie on the ground beside her. The small, triangular wing bases, the wing scales, as they are called, remain on her thorax for the rest of her life and make it easy to recognise her as a primary queen, the foundress of the colony.

As soon as she has deprived herself of her wings she raises the tip of her abdomen and it seems certain that, when she does this,

PLATE VII

(*a*) Short-winged grey nymphs, with workers

These may be found in the nests at any time of the year. They are about a quarter of an inch long

(*b*) Secondary queens and a secondary king, with workers

These develop from short-winged grey nymphs and replace the old king and queen

PLATE VIII

(*a*) Short-winged grey nymphs

These are older than those shown on Plate VII (*a*). The resting stage of
the red mite, *Cosmoglyphus kramerii*, can be seen on the nymph at the right;
the two round black dots on the head are not eyes, but mites.

(*b*) A tertiary queen of the black-mound termite, with workers
in attendance

She is only about a quarter of an inch long

she gives off a scent which is imperceptible to our blunted sense of smell but that is perceived by the males at a distance. In the meantime, other males and females have settled on the ground and herbage in the vicinity and dropped their wings and they run about, the females with the tip of the abdomen raised and the males seeking eagerly. If a male is watched he will be seen to run a devious course, but in the general direction of a female near him, until he touches her with his antennæ. The pair of them then line up, tandem fashion, with her in front and him close behind, and they move off together in search of their new home.

If, whilst they are running in this way, you hold the male down with a match-stick or grass-stalk and prevent him from following her, you will find that she will stop and wait for him to catch up with her again. If two pairs are guided so that their paths cross it is easy to manœuvre an exchange of partners; the males do not mind what females they follow and the females are also indifferent; any partner of the opposite sex will do. With a little patience you may succeed in getting two or three males to follow one female, but such an unnatural procession soon breaks up. You will not succeed in any attempts to get a female to follow a male; she must always be in the lead.

If some winged termites are taken from a nest before the nuptial flight and they are put in a box together, they do not shed their wings and pair. They must have the stimulus of the nuptial flight before the other actions can follow in orderly sequence. Even a short flight of a yard or so is enough. Sometimes nuptial flights have taken place from mounds that I have brought into my laboratory in the autumn, and the males and females have all flown directly to the brightest window. There many of them have dropped their wings and some of them have paired in the usual manner, although they have only flown a few feet. The great majority of them, however, flutter against the glass and run about without shedding their wings. For a brief period they are strongly attracted towards the light, but this changes as soon as they have lost their wings and paired—then they seek darkness again as soon as they can.

Copulation does not take place when a pair forms after the nuptial flight. The two move off over the veld until the female finds a spot which she regards as suitable for her home. She takes the initiative in this and he meekly follows. Having found a stone or half-buried piece of wood, the female begins to dig in the damp soil and he may or may not attempt to help. In any case, by far the greater part of the digging is done by her and she soon sinks a shaft beside the stone or wood and the two of them disappear into it, returning to the darkness from which they came, their elaborate provision of eyes no longer of any use to them. Two inches or so below the surface a small chamber about half an inch in diameter is hollowed out and here the pair take up their abode, blocking the tunnel behind them with soil removed in making the chamber. There they remain, idle and motionless, all through the winter, and it is probable that copulation does not take place until the arrival of warmer weather in the spring.

Their perils are by no means over. Many of the couples are flooded out and killed by the heavy winter rains; many are devoured by such subterranean enemies as the peculiar burrowing frogs, *Breviceps* species, that live on the mountain slopes and never go near water (Plate XIVa), the pink burrowing snake, *Typhlops delalandii*, the golden mole, *Chrysochloris asiatica*, and other smaller foes of the abundant cryptobiotic fauna of the south-west Cape. Very few indeed of the thousands that leave the mounds in the autumn survive to the following spring. During the succeeding summer months drought seems to be the greatest danger to the survivors. If weeks go by without rain, then the young kings and queens are killed by the dry atmosphere in their ill-protected cells. In some areas and some years the whole nuptial flight may be a complete failure and not one couple may survive. That is why, when walking over the veld, you may fail to find a single small mound in certain places, although large mounds are numerous; in other places young colonies may be common; in the former case, the nuptial flights have met with disaster for a few years running, whilst in the latter they have been more successful. In those parts of the Cape where that pernicious pest, the Argentine ant, *Iridomyrmex humilis*, has established itself you will not find any young termitaries at all, because the ants seek out the termites and destroy them; only old, well-guarded mounds can persist in the presence of these destructive little creatures. The mounds also disappear from ground that is being cultivated or built upon; they are found only on raw, untouched veld, and there they are often destroyed by veld fires. The result of all this is that the black-mound termite is getting scarcer year by year and one has to go higher and higher up the mountains to find their nests.

The young queen's abdomen swells very little during the first year of her career. She lays some half a dozen eggs in September and she and her mate spend their whole time brooding over them. They do not leave the nest at all for food or water. In order to watch the development of the new colonies I have isolated many pairs in glass receptacles of soil in the laboratory, but they do not thrive under these conditions. Sooner or later they eat their eggs and they die. This is almost certainly due to my failure to provide them with the degree of humidity and ventilation that they require.

Much better results were obtained when pairs were isolated in small earthenware flower-pots of soil. These were kept covered with glass lids in the laboratory until the termites had established themselves in their cells and then the pots were buried to two-thirds of their depth in the garden outside. The young kings and queens were protected from attack by ants by a sprinkling of ten per cent. D.D.T. powder round each pot. Most of the pairs survived under these more natural conditions and after this it was only necessary for me to examine the contents of the pots from time to time throughout the succeeding months in order to learn the progress of the young colonies.

By this method it was learned that the establishment of a new colony is a slow process. At the end of the first year the queen is only about seven millimetres long and her abdomen is still slender and white, and her family consists of only a dozen or so stunted workers. The further growth of the colony and the queen has been described elsewhere (see Figures 4 and 14) and there is no need to say more here, except to add that the appearance of the king does not change as he grows older. He retains his youthful slenderness and can move about as nimbly as the workers; he hides himself very cleverly and is difficult to find when a mound is broken open.

## Chapter Nine

# THE SUCCESSION TO THE THRONE

W E must now return to those short-winged grey nymphs mentioned in the previous chapter (Figure 17) and learn what happens to them. They may be found in the nests at any time of the year, even in the heart of winter, whereas the long-winged white nymphs are only present during late summer. Almost invariably, when a termitary is broken open, some of these grey nymphs may be seen running about among the workers; it may be only half a dozen or so in a small mound or two or three hundred in a large one. It is easy to pick them out by their colour and their short wing-pads; they are the same size as the white nymphs, about six millimetres long (Plate VIIa). They go out with the workers foraging for food, which is something that the white nymphs never do.

If a grey nymph is dissected its gut is found to contain coarse food particles similar to those found in the alimentary canal of adult workers. Whereas the white nymphs are fed on predigested food by the workers all their lives, the grey nymphs are compelled to take solid, untreated food during the penultimate instar, and that is why their abdomens darken in colour. Obviously they are sexual nymphs, but there is something peculiar about their development and this seems to be due to the nature of their food. They are prevented from growing up normally into winged adults and they can remain in the arrested, short-winged stage for months if necessary. I have kept them alive in my observation nests for over a year without any change. They are kept in reserve in the termitary in case any accident should befall the king and queen.

If some of these grey nymphs are present in one of my artificial nests, and if I take away the king and queen and then provide the colony with an abundance of food, within three or four weeks some of the nymphs begin to swell and within six weeks they are converted into secondary kings and queens to replace their lost father and mother. They do not cast their skin and become mature in the ordinary way, but their sexual organs develop and much fatty tissue is laid down in their abdomens, due apparently to the extra care and attention given to them by the workers. The skin of the head and thorax turns brown, the eyes darken and the abdomen assumes a pale yellow tinge; the wing-pads remain small and may even shrink whilst these changes are going on (Plate VIIb). A dozen or more secondary kings and queens may be produced to take the place of the primary pair. If there are no grey nymphs in the nest when the primary king and queen are taken away, but only workers, soldiers and long-winged white nymphs, then no secondary reproductives appear.

When mounds are opened on the veld about twenty per cent. of them are found to contain secondary kings and queens, therefore the original pair, the founders of the colony, must often be lost for some reason or other. Probably the most frequent cause for the disappearance of the old reproductives is that they are put to death because of waning fertility. The primary king and queen are always replaced by several pairs of secondaries, probably because the latter are less fertile than the former. I have counted as many as thirty-five secondary queens and twenty-nine males from one nest. In another mound I found only one secondary queen and over forty males; something had obviously gone wrong with the economy of this termitary and far more supplementary kings had been produced than necessary. Only once have I found a nest where a primary queen was present with secondary reproductives, and she was old and feeble. For some reason her life had been spared longer than usual. This case is important because of its bearing on the problem of the origin of the different castes, which is discussed in a later chapter.

The secondary reproductives are easily recognised by the short wing-pads on their backs, instead of the small triangular wing-scales seen on the backs of the primaries. Also their eyes are smaller and their heads are brown instead of black. I find that secondary kings and queens are readily accepted if taken from one colony and offered to another that already has some; in this way I have installed as many as fifty queens and fifty kings in one nest. The secondaries are fed and groomed and licked by the workers just like the primaries.

Beside the primary and secondary reproductives, there is a third type of king and queen one may find if one hunts long enough. These tertiary reproductives are much rarer than the

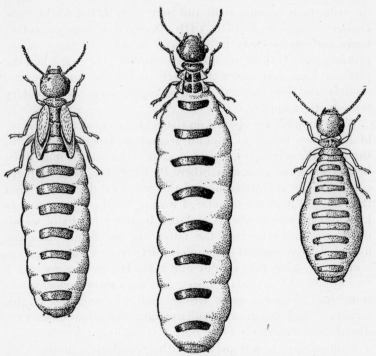

Fig. 21.—The Three Types of Queens found in the Nests of the Black-Mound Termite. Primary queen in the middle, secondary queen on the left, tertiary queen on the right. All drawn to the same scale. The young primary queen shown is about half an inch long.

others. Out of two hundred or so mounds that I have broken up in the course of my investigations, only three of them contained tertiary kings and queens. In all three cases the colonies were few in numbers, although they occupied large mounds, which were mainly empty, with the surviving members of formerly prosperous colonies living in comparatively few cells near the bases of the mounds.

In one of the nests there were two tertiary queens and a king, in another I found only one king and queen, but in the third there were fifteen queens and ten kings. In each case more might have been present, but these tertiaries are not much larger than the workers, being only about six millimetres in length, or a little less than a quarter of an inch, and they run about actively and are difficult to find. They are pale yellow in

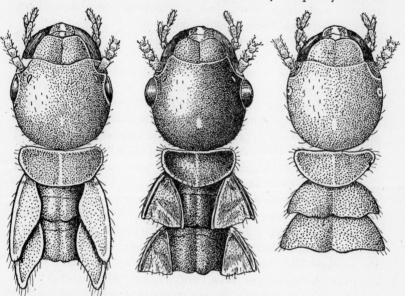

FIG. 22.—Head and Thorax of the Three Types of Reproductives. Primary reproductive in the middle, with wing-scales and fully developed eyes; secondary reproductive on left, with wing-pads and smaller eyes; tertiary reproductive on right, without wings and with tiny, vestigial eyes. There is no difference between the head and thorax of king and queen.

colour, with brown heads and very small, vestigial eyes. There are no wing-pads on their backs but the second and third segments of the thorax have jutting corners, like those seen in young sexual nymphs when the wings first begin to develop. The male and female are alike, except that her abdomen is a little more bulky than his (Plates VIIIb and IXa).

All three of the colonies that contained these tertiaries were obviously on the verge of extinction and the presence of this type of reproductive indicates a last desperate attempt on the part of the termites to ward off the inevitable end of what had once been teeming citadels. When these colonies were removed to the laboratory and installed in observation nests, it was seen that the workers feed and groom their tertiary kings and queens in the usual manner, but they pay less attention to them than to primary or secondary reproductives. They run about actively and signal alarm just as vigorously as the workers. After a few weeks these colonies died out.

Although secondary reproductives are rather difficult to find in a state of nature, it is possible to obtain them by the following method: A large mound is broken up and the inhabitants shaken out on to a sheet of glass. Then the broken pieces of the mound are put into eight-inch earthenware flower-pots, nearly filling each pot. After this ten thousand or so termites are dumped into each pot. In this way a large colony is divided into several lots and the composition of each lot can be varied as one wishes. For example, the king and queen, with about ten thousand members of their family, can be placed in one pot, in order to see how they restore their broken home and build up their numbers again. In another pot, only adult workers and soldiers are placed, to learn how long they can live. In a third, short-winged grey nymphs are included with the workers and soldiers, in order to obtain secondary reproductives. A fourth pot may contain only adult workers and soldiers, with young in different stages of development, and so on.

These pots, with their contents, are buried to about two-thirds of their depth in suitable spots in the garden and the inhabitants are protected from ants by the method already mentioned, D.D.T. powder. The termites soon settle down and rebuild their broken home and they enter the soil through the hole at the bottom of each pot and forage for themselves. I have had dozens of such pots under observation for months and, provided I can keep the ants out, the termites do very well in them. It is the first two or three days after the pots are put out in the garden that is the dangerous period, until the termites have succeeded in closing up all the openings and have fastened the broken pieces of mound together and cemented them to the inside of the pot. After this the ants cannot get at them, and they are more secure inside the pots than they are in their natural homes. The porous walls of the pots admit the moisture and air that they need and the termites take very well to their new abodes after they have got over the shock of the installation.

One can leave the termites in the pots as long as one wishes and after this it is easy to turn them out and see what has

FIG. 23.—The Three Types of Kings of the Black-Mound Termite. Primary king in the middle, with wing-scales and fully developed eyes; secondary king on the left, with wing-pads and small eyes; tertiary king on the right, without wings and with tiny vestigial eyes. All drawn to the same scale. They are about a quarter of an inch long.

happened to them. By this simple method I have produced as many secondary reproductives as I wished. I find that secondaries appear only in those pots that have short-winged grey nymphs included among their inhabitants.

In an attempt to produce tertiary reproductives, twenty-five batches of adult workers and soldiers, together with a large number of eggs and young, were isolated in pots during the summer and placed outside the laboratory in the soil. When these were opened two or three months later it was found that in each case the eggs and young had been eaten, probably because of the violent upset caused by the breaking up of the mounds and the sorting out of the inhabitants. It is possible that some of the young had matured in the interval, but there was no way of determining this. No tertiaries were found in these pots, only adult workers and soldiers were present.

All this is part of the fascinating problem of the origin of the different castes among termites and further discussion of it is reserved for a later chapter.

## Chapter Ten

## FEEDING THE MULTITUDE

IT is well known that termites destroy wood, that they feed on dead and decaying vegetation of various kinds, unattractive materials that most other living creatures will not touch. Because their food material is abundant and because there is little competition for it, these insects are exceedingly numerous in areas where climatic conditions are suitable for them. Apart from micro-organisms, termites are far and away the most numerous of living creatures in Africa and they teem almost everywhere in the soil. It may be said that they own Africa in a truer sense than do the human inhabitants, that they were here long before man arrived and that they will probably be here long after he, through his folly, has gone. They perform an important function in nature, similar to that performed by earthworms in cooler parts of the globe; they break down tough cellulose materials and bring them back into circulation, making them available for the use of other animals and plants.

To say, however, that termites eat wood, that cellulose forms the major part of their diet, is by no means a full or satisfactory answer. The more primitive types among them certainly live in dead timber and devour it, but even in their case there are always fungi and bacteria in their burrows and these seem to form part of their food. Furthermore, cellulose is very indigestible and few animals can deal with it; cattle and other grass-eating animals need enormous numbers of bacteria and other micro-organisms in their alimentary canal to help them deal with their food. It is the same with the primitive, wood-eating termites; their guts are crammed with amazing parasites without which they cannot digest their food (Figure 32). The higher termites, including the black-mound termite, lack these cellulose-digesting parasites, therefore it would seem that they cannot utilise sound, woody material as food. The harvester termites gather grass, but they do not eat it in the fresh state;

they carry it into their nests and treat it in some manner about which we know nothing. Some of the most highly developed of all termites, the fungus-growers, include some of the worst pests that destroy timber in our houses, but they do not get their nourishment from it. They chew up the wood and swallow it and then, deep down in their nests, they make the strange fungus beds that look something like large walnut kernels, out of the chewed wood and excrement, and on these they skilfully cultivate the tiny white balls of fungus that form the major part of their food (Plate Xb). In short, we know very little indeed about the exact nature of the food of most termites.

If you walk over the mountain slopes where the nests of the black-mound termite are found and if you try to ascertain the nature of their food, you will find that you are confronted by a difficult problem. There are no signs at all of any depredations on the vegetation around and near the mounds. The insects do not attack living plants at all—in fact, you will often see heaths and reeds and other plants growing right through the mounds and in a flourishing condition. Dead branches, twigs and leaves lying on the ground are not touched, but you will sometimes find them nibbling at the surface of dead roots and stumps buried in the ground. They do not burrow into the dead timber as some species of termites do. Occasionally you will find some workers under a cow-pat that is drying in the sun, and when you lift up stones you may find some of their burrows just beneath them. Wandering over the veld and probing into the soil teaches you very little about the nature of their food.

This is an important problem because so much hangs upon it. If we knew more about the diet of termites, about their likes and dislikes, we should probably be able to deal more effectively with those species that do so much damage in our buildings. Also the problem of caste differentiation is closely linked with that of feeding and we shall not be able to throw any light on the one without a greater knowledge of the other. In order to find out exactly what the black-mound termites eat I had to learn how to keep them alive in the laboratory under more or less natural conditions, in such a way that I could offer them various materials and watch their reactions. This was not easy but, after many failures, I succeeded in devising some simple pieces of apparatus that gave interesting results. These are described and figured in the last chapter of this book (Plates XII and XIII).

One great advantage of working with termites that live in small mounds lies in the ease with which they can be removed, complete with their inhabitants, and carried into the laboratory. A termitary of the black-mound termite eight or nine inches high and about ten years old weighs only twenty pounds or so and can be transported long distances by train, car or 'plane without harm to the inhabitants and it is very suitable for experimental purposes. This species is not a pest and has no economic importance, therefore there is no danger of causing trouble by carrying it into areas where it is not normally found. I have kept literally millions alive in my laboratory over a period of years and they do no damage at all. One large termitary was sent by sea to England and it arrived in good condition, with the termites alive and flourishing, but they eventually died out through wrong treatment.

Apparatus similar to that shown in Figures 38 and 39 on pages 124, 126 were used in the feeding experiments and about a dozen medium-sized mounds were kept going in the laboratory at a time. Dead twigs of all kinds of plants found in the vicinity of the mounds were offered in the glass tubes (Figure 39), and thin cross sections of larger branches of proteas, heaths and other indigenous bushes and trees were placed in the flat food-chambers (Figure 38). Also various grasses and reedlike plants (*Restionaceæ* and *Cyperaceæ*, that are so abundant on the mountain slopes of the south-west Cape), as well as mosses, lichens, liverworts, fungi—in fact, every kind of plant available was tried. All this was sound, dead material moistened with water, but the termites would not eat it, nor would they touch the filter paper offered to them. They nibbled a little at the bark of some of the twigs and they drank from the moist surfaces, but lengthy experiments showed that they do not feed on sound, dead vegetable matter, nor on pure cellulose such as is found in filter paper and cotton wool.

Sawdust from various kinds of wood, thin rectangles of several different timbers, rectangles of cardboard and paper were also offered and all were ignored. Slices of potato, carrot, turnip, beetroot, banana and apple did not attract them except that, when very hungry, they ate the hard, central core of the carrot slices. They starved in the presence of white and brown bread, biscuits, cake, whole meal and white meal, maize meal and different kinds of cereal breakfast foods. Never in the long history of their kind have termites had such a choice of nourishing foods placed before them, but they showed no interest in any of them.

But when decayed wood was placed in the food-chambers the scene changed. The workers crowded into them and fed greedily. They prefer the wood when it is so badly decayed that it is soft enough to be broken up in the fingers—punk, as it is called. They accepted most kinds of punk offered to them, decayed branches and roots of proteas and heaths, acacias, fruit trees, willow, poplar, oak, and so on. They will not feed on the punk when it is dry; it must be moist and they prefer it when it is damp, not soggy.

The favourite food of the black-mound termite, however, consists of the decayed stems of the reedlike plants belonging to the family *Restionaceæ*. This family of plants is confined mainly to South Africa and Australia, only a few isolated species being found elsewhere. Over eighty different species are recorded from the Cape alone. They have numerous slender, cylindrical stems two or three feet long, with flowering spikes at the tips, mostly reddish brown in colour with conspicuous brown bracts, male flowers being borne on one plant and female flowers on another. Very few insects attack them in the living state. The leaves are very small or absent altogether.

After the plants have flowered the stems dry and stand in dense clumps that form one of the major fire hazards on the mountain slopes during the hot dry summer months. A match carelessly dropped on one of these clumps when a cigarette is lighted, or the embers of a picnicker's fire blowing on to them can easily start a blaze that may spread for miles before it is stopped. Eventually, if they are not burned, the stems fall to the ground and there they rot and form an important part of the termite's food.

The black-mound termites do not like completely decayed vegetable matter in the form of humus or leaf-mould. They take it when it is partially decomposed, whilst the stems have still retained their original form but are soft enough to be rubbed through a coarse sieve. They will also eat sun-dried cow-dung and horse-dung, after it has been washed and sifted, but they do this only with reluctance and when no other food is available. Elephant dung, brought all the way from the Kruger National Park by car, was also accepted, but without eagerness, as well as tortoise droppings.

Fig. 24.—The Food of the Black-Mound Termite. Flowering spikes of some Cape species of *Restionaceæ*, natural size. The termites eat the decayed stems of these plants.

These preliminary tests showed, then, that three types of food could conveniently be used for further feeding experiments: decayed vegetation of *Restionaceæ* is readily accepted, punk of various kinds is eaten freely but is not as popular as the first, and dung of herbivorous animals is taken only when they are very hungry. After this it was only necessary to add different substances to these materials in order to find out what would attract them and what repel them.

At first sight this endeavour to find out exactly what the

termites eat, what they like and what they don't like, might seem a poor way of spending one's time, but it is a subject that has important aspects. In the first place, we want to learn how to deal with those species that are serious pests and that cause such heavy damage to timber in buildings and to pasturage on the veld; we want to know how they can be destroyed or repelled in an efficient and economic manner. The methods used hitherto in trying to determine what will kill or deter termites are slow, laborious and unsatisfactory. For example, there is the method known as the "graveyard test." Pieces of wood two or three feet long and a few inches wide and an inch or so thick, are soaked in the materials to be tested and then they are buried to half their depth in soil that is known to be infested with termites. These posts sticking out of the ground form the "graveyards." After some weeks or months they are pulled up again and examined for the extent of the damage done to them. In a second type of tests, small pegs of wood are treated with poisons or repellents and then holes are bored in them and a small number of wood-inhabiting termites placed in each peg. After a time the pegs are opened to learn what has happened to the insects and how much damage they have done. A third method consists of placing termites in flat glass dishes with moist filter paper and dusting them with the poisons to be tested.

The simple pieces of apparatus described in the last chapter of this book offer much better methods of finding out what the effects of various substances are on the termites, what attracts and what repels them, what kills them and what leaves them unharmed. They are methods that can be adapted to any species that live in termitaries that can be readily removed and carried into the laboratory, and there are many such species found all through the warmer areas of the globe. The methods should also prove useful in throwing light on that vexed problem of the origin of the castes.

The flat food-chambers used in the major experiments, shown in Figures 38 and 39, measured five inches by four inches, or four and a quarter inches by three and a quarter inches, because I happened to have a number of old photographic negatives of these sizes that made useful covers when cleaned.

PLATE IX

(*a*) Tertiary king of the black-mound termite, with workers in attendance

He is about the same size as the workers

(*b*) The Malmesbury termite, *Microcerotermes malmesburyi*

Queen with workers and alates. The workers are little more than an eighth of an inch long.

PLATE X

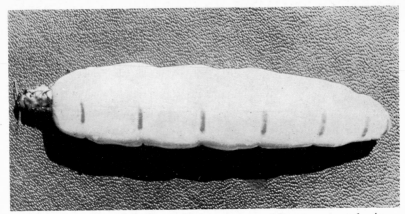

(*a*) The queen of the large fungus-grower, *Macrotermes natalensis*
She is about four inches long. Unlike the queen of the black-mound termite, she is kept a prisoner in a thick-walled royal cell deep down in the nest.

(*b*) One of the fungus gardens of the fungus-growing termite, *Macrotermes natalensis*
The termites eat the little white balls of fungus that grow on their beds. The match-stick shows the comparative size.

Each of these chambers, three-eighths of an inch deep, will hold twenty-five cubic centimetres of food comfortably and there is still plenty of room for the workers to move about in them. This quantity, then, was adopted as the standard when the chambers were replenished and a small container was made that held this amount, for use in measuring out the food, and a record was kept of the volume of food the termites ate. Even in winter, when little activity is going on, it is astonishing how much a flourishing colony will devour. A mound about fifteen inches high and containing some 20,000 inhabitants, when fed on moist, untreated food (decayed *Restionaceæ* and punk) emptied all twelve food-chambers around their nest every ten days, on the average, during the winter. This meant that they were eating thirty cubic centimetres of food daily whilst they were all moving about little and idling their time away. When the warmer weather arrived in spring they became more active and the food-chambers needed replenishing every three or four days. Later still, when there were young in the nest, they had to be given fresh food supplies every other day and the whole colony was devouring about 200 cubic centimetres of food daily. Over a period of three months, from September to November, this termitary took approximately 10,000 cubic centimetres of food and it is reasonable to assume that about 40,000 cubic centimetres would be required in a year. This represents a volume equal to a cube with sides about fourteen inches long, that is to say, a volume roughly equal to that of the mound itself.

Now, 20,000 black-mound termites occupy a volume of about 80 cubic centimetres (see page 23), therefore it may be said that they devour 500 times their own volume of food in a year. Or to put it in another way, 20,000 of the insects eat 40,000 cubic centimetres of food, therefore each one takes approximately 2 cubic centimetres in a year. This may seem little, but when one remembers how very abundant they are one begins to realise the important part they play in nature. In many parts of Africa termite mounds are thickly dotted over the veld and the amount of dead vegetation the insects consume must be enormous. This is probably one of the reasons why most soils in Africa are lacking in humus; the termites leave

6

little vegetation to rot. If the grass-eating termites, such as the harvester termites, *Hodotermes* species, and the snouted harvesters, *Trinervitermes* species, eat comparable amounts of food, then they must be very destructive to the pasturage in areas where they occur.

Termites must often have difficulty in finding sufficient food for their needs in a state of nature. The decaying vegetation they require is sparsely scattered and they are slow-moving insects, taking two hours to travel to a point twenty-five yards from their nest and back at twenty-five degrees Centigrade (see page 29). This difficulty of the food supply, it would seem, is the chief if not the only factor that limits the size of their colonies. It may also be the reason why, after thirty years or so, the colonies dwindle and eventually die out. The veld fires that are so prevalent throughout Africa during the dry season, besides helping to convert the whole continent into a desert, must also play an important part in limiting the food supply of the termites.

The next task in these feeding experiments was to try the addition of various substances to the food in order to learn whether these additions made it more or less attractive. Five sugars, the only ones available to me, were tried—sucrose, fructose, glucose, rhamnose and xylose. It was found that food sweetened with any of these was made more attractive than when water alone was added. The time taken to empty the food-chambers gave an indication of the comparative popularity of the different sugars. The chambers containing food moistened with sucrose and fructose solutions were emptied most quickly, glucose came next, then rhamnose, and xylose was a long way behind, being visited with little more eagerness than food moistened with water only. The order in which the termites chose the sugars was about the same order as that of their degree of sweetness according to human taste, therefore it would seem that the sense of taste in termites in this respect is about the same as our own. It was found that the food sweetened with sucrose or fructose was taken nearly twice as quickly as that with glucose, three or four times as fast as that with rhamnose, more than six times as fast as the xylose, and about ten times as quickly as food moistened with water only. Cane sugar has definitely a strong attraction for them. The strength of the solution added to the food is not critical; they seem to prefer it when it is pleasantly sweet according to human taste, but they don't like it when it is strong and syrupy, possibly because the food is then sticky to their feet.

Seven kinds of starch were tested, potato, wheat, rice, maize, arrowroot, sago and tapioca. Suspensions of starch grains in water were poured on the food and thoroughly mixed and it was found that the addition of these made the food more attractive than when water alone was added, but less attractive than when sweetened with sucrose or fructose. The termites took the food fortified with starch as readily as they accepted it with glucose, and they showed no preference for one kind of starch over another.

All the vitamins that were available were tried, A, the B complex, C, D, E and K, by mixing them in varying proportions with their food. It was found that A and D repelled them, but this was probably due more to the oily medium than to the vitamins themselves. The addition of yeast to their food did not make it more attractive, and they showed no interest in thiamine, nicotinic acid or riboflavine when these were added separately. This is strange because other investigators have shown that the B complex is an essential ingredient of the food of most insects, but termites probably get all they need from the bacteria in their food. The only vitamin to which they gave a positive reaction was C, and they took this eagerly. In each of my nests one food-chamber contained filter paper that was kept moistened with water so that the insects could drink if they wished. Numbers of workers were generally to be seen standing on the damp paper, with their mouthparts applied to it and obviously drinking; they do not eat the paper. When ascorbic acid is added, many more termites visit the chambers and they may nibble small holes in the paper moistened with the solution. Food moistened with water in which vitamin C is dissolved, or with water and orange juice or guava juice, is more attractive than food without this addition.

After these tests it was possible to make up a food that they accepted more eagerly than anything else. This consisted of decayed vegetation (mostly *Restionaceæ* and punk rubbed through a coarse sieve), moistened with water in which sufficient sucrose was dissolved to make it pleasantly sweet to the taste, with about 0·1 gramme of ascorbic acid added to each pint of water. The amount of sugar and vitamin C is not critical. Black-mound termites flourish on this mixture and it was used in all the subsequent tests.

One of the problems connected with the diet of termites is the source of their nitrogenous food. From where do they get their proteins? The materials that provide them with nourishment seem to be generally lacking in nitrogen. In an attempt to throw some light on this problem various amino-acids were added to the food. These included methionine, asparagine, lysine, leucine, alanine, typtophane, aspartic acid, glutamic acid, phenylalanine, voline, norleucine, cystine, tyrosine, norvaline, serine and arginine, all substances from which proteins are built up and some of which have been proved to be essential for normal health and growth of higher animals. But the termites showed no interest in any of them. They accepted food to which they were added in small quantities, but they were repelled if the solutions or suspensions mixed with their food were too strong, and in every case they preferred their meals without the amino-acids.

A few drugs that were available were added to the food to find out what effect they had on the insects. They will take dicoumarol, the anti-coagulant that will kill mammals and that is used as a rat poison, and they show no signs of any illeffects. They will eat food impregnated with aspirin (one tablet containing 0·324 gramme of acetylsalicylic acid mixed with twenty-five cubic centimetres of water) and such a diet prolonged over a period of four months appeared to leave them healthy and unaffected. They seemed to be less responsive to light and to signal less freely after a few days of this food, but the effect was slight and did not increase as time went on.

The female sex hormone œstrogen, in the form of the synthetic products, ethinyl-œstradiol, dienœstrol and stilbœstrol, as well as the synthetic male hormone, methyltestosterone, were tried and the termites accepted them. In each case the tablets, containing from 0·02 to 10 milligrammes of the hormone, were crushed in water sweetened with cane sugar and added to the food, which was eaten as readily as food without the hormone.

In order to learn whether these mammalian hormones had any effect on the sexual development of the termites, three mounds were broken up and the kings and queens removed. The broken mounds, together with their inmates, were then placed in receptacles as shown in Figure 38, and the insects soon settled down. Within four or five days they entered the food-chambers and began to feed on the material impregnated with the hormones. One nest was kept as a control and received only sweetened food. In this colony, as well as in one of the other two, a number of short-winged grey nymphs were present, whilst in the third there were no such nymphs, but plenty of young, undifferentiated termites. At the end of three months the nests were broken up again and examined. There were secondary kings and queens in both the nests that had had short-winged grey nymphs in them, and the addition of hormones to the food appeared to have had no effects at all. In the third nest, without the short-winged nymphs, there were no reproductives and the young had disappeared; either they had all developed into adult workers and soldiers, or they had been killed and eaten.

## Chapter Eleven

## UNINVITED GUESTS

LIKE other social animals, termites are much exploited by parasites and uninvited guests. All sorts of curious creatures have been found in the nests of these insects in different parts of the world, and the black-mound termite is no exception. If the mounds of this species are broken open during the summer months, soft, white maggots will be found in some of them. There may be two dozen or more in a nest, or only a few, or none at all. They are very small in November and reach full size by the end of April, when they are thirteen to fifteen millimetres, or three-fifths of an inch, in length, pointed at the front end and rounded behind (Plate XIa).

These maggots creep about slowly from cell to cell in the mound and they can squeeze through the small openings connecting the cells. They are attended by workers that groom them and feed them much in the same way as they care for their queen. It seems certain that the termites get from the maggots some exudation of which they are fond and, in return for this, they not only tolerate their presence in the nest but treat them like honoured guests or pampered pets. If some of the maggots are taken from a mound and offered to another colony in an observation nest, they are eagerly accepted and adopted and they make themselves at home at once in their new abode.

If one of these maggots is hungry it raises its head and waves it to and fro; immediately one of the attendant workers runs to it and, mouth to mouth, supplies it with predigested food apparently similar to that given to young termites and to the king and queen. The soft-bodied maggots are very delicate and they die in a short time if removed from the sheltered conditions of the nest.

When the larva is fully grown in the autumn it makes its way towards the exterior of the mound and there, in an oval cell about half an inch below the outer surface, generally somewhere near the top of the mound, it pupates. As is the case with many other kinds of flies, it does not cast its skin when it pupates, but its body thickens and shortens and becomes rounded at each end and the skin hardens and turns reddish brown and forms a case for the pupa, known as the puparium. Inside this case the pupa is formed. The puparium fits snugly in its cell in the hard material of the mound and it is a mystery how the weak, soft maggot manages to hollow out this retreat for itself.

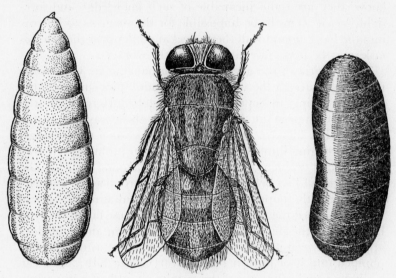

Fig. 25.—The Guest Fly of the Black-Mound Termite, *Termitometopia skaifei* Zumpt. Adult fly in the middle, larva on left, puparium on right. The fly is about the size of a blow fly and dark grey in colour.

The tiny jaws, like a pair of minute hooks inside the pore that serves it as a mouth, are obviously useless as digging implements in material that is so hard it requires a blow from a hatchet to break it. The first autumn rains, that arrive at the time when the larvæ are pupating, may soften the outer wall of the mound but even then it would be too hard for the maggots to penetrate it, yet they do so and they lie in neat, smooth-walled cells that fit them like gloves.

It is possible that the worker termites hollow out the pupation cells for their pets, but I have seen no evidence of this. If they do so, then it would seem as though they are aware of the future needs of their pets and of what is going to happen to them. The cells are dug out of exactly the right size and shape and near enough to the surface to make it as easy as possible for the flies to escape into the open air, and yet at the same time deep enough below the surface to afford the inmates protection and shelter. It would be nonsense to assume that the termites reason all this out and act accordingly; as far as we know, they are quite incapable of such knowledge and foresight. Yet it seems to be impossible for the maggots to burrow into the hard mound wall themselves and it looks as though this task must be performed for them by the workers.

The puparia of the guest fly lie dormant in the wall of the mound all through the winter and the adult flies emerge in the following spring, in September and October. Here again it is difficult to understand how they break their way out to the exterior. The flies are very feeble creatures when they emerge, with no digging implements to aid them in pushing their way through half an inch or more of the hard mound wall. All the many kinds of flies belonging to the same group as the guest fly escape from the puparium by means of a pulsating bladder in the head, called the ptilinum. When one of these flies is ready to break out of the pupal case its head splits open and a bladder appears between its eyes which goes in and out as the blood is pumped into it or from it by the heart (Plate XIb). This can easily be seen in the case of the termite guest fly if a puparium is placed in a glass tube just wide enough to hold it and if the tube is then filled with fine sand. When the adult escapes from the puparium it makes its way up through the sand by means of its ptilinum, thrusting it in and out all the time to push the sand grains aside as it struggles upwards. This amazing method of using a bladder of blood in the head as a battering ram can be watched through a hand lens; it is a slow, laborious process and the fly may take an hour or more to thrust its way up through two inches of dry sand. After it has succeeded in reaching the open air the bladder is withdrawn, the slit in the head closes, the soft, crumpled wings expand and stiffen and harden, and then the insect is able to fly away.

When the puparia are put into tubes of sand the flies make

their escape, but if the tubes are plugged with pieces of mound material half an inch thick, they fail to break their way through these barriers, although they ram at them persistently until they die of exhaustion. Therefore I do not know how the flies make their way out of the mound. Maybe the termites help them in this also. As a matter of fact, the only specimens of this insect known to science are the few that I have reared in my laboratory. They have so far not been seen or caught in the open. The specimens were sent to Dr. F. Zumpt, a South African specialist on flies, and he found that they belong to a new genus and species and he named them *Termitometopia skaifei*, paying me the dubious compliment of naming the maggots after me.

The fly is about two-fifths of an inch long, dark grey with lighter patches on the body. It is a feeble flier and many of those reared in the laboratory failed to expand their wings. Nothing at all is known about their habits or their method of oviposition, where, when and how they lay their eggs. Those that I reared refused the honey and sugar-water offered to them and they died in a few days. The group to which they belong, the *Sarcophaginæ*, is a very large one and includes many species found in all parts of the world. The larvæ have very different habits; some live in carrion, others in dung, many are parasitic and destroy caterpillars, grasshoppers, beetles, scorpions, earthworms, and some have even been found in the skin of tortoises and the stomachs of frogs, whilst a few cause great distress by infesting wounds and may even get into the nasal passages and other parts of the human body. So far no other species of the *Sarcophaginæ* have been found in termites' nests, although more than twenty kinds of flies belonging to other families are known as guests of termites in various parts of the world.

Another uninvited guest that is common in the nests of the black-mound termite as well as of other species of termites throughout Africa, is the little white spring-tail, *Cyphoderus arcuatus*. This tiny insect is only about one twenty-fifth of an inch long and it runs about freely inside the termitary, never getting on to the termites but dodging about among their feet. Living in perpetual darkness, it does not need eyes and is quite blind, yet it twists and turns most skilfully so as to avoid contact with its hosts as it moves about, and the termites ignore it completely, probably being quite unaware of its presence.

Usually a number of these little creatures may be found in a prosperous colony, it may be fifty or a hundred or more, and they are in all stages of growth, from newly hatched young to adults. They are very primitive insects and are probably of more ancient origin than even the termites themselves. They belong to the order *Collembola* which includes many species of small insects found all over the world, usually in damp spots,

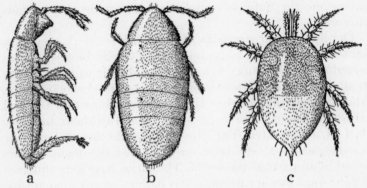

a                        b                        c

Fig. 26.—Uninvited Guests of the Black-Mound Termite: (*a*) the white spring-tail, *Cyphoderus arcuatus*, side view, (*b*) the same, viewed from above, (*c*) the white mite, *Termitacarus cuneiformis*.

but because of their insignificant size and appearance they attract little attention. Their popular name, spring-tails, is given to them because of the curious leaping organ each one carries at the hind end of the underside of the abdomen. When not in use, this is carried bent forward under the abdomen and the forked tip is held in place by a pair of tiny hooks called the retinaculum.

If the spring-tail wishes to jump, this forked organ is released from the catch and it sweeps downwards and backwards until it projects behind like a tail. This action causes the spring to strike against the ground and the insect is jerked into the air. If the spring-tails are removed from the nest and teased, they will jump, but they seem to have no control over the direction

of the leaps and are just as likely to land on their backs as on
their feet. Inside the narrow confines of the cells of the nest they
never seem to jump, but run about nimbly.

It is not known what they eat, but they are probably scavengers. There seems to be little for them to scavenge inside the
termitary, but they may feed on the debris left over when the
workers devour the corpses. The workers don't eat the hard
skulls of their dead and I have seen the little spring-tails
investigating these before they were carried away by the
workers to the rubbish heap somewhere in the outer confines of
the nest.

One mystery concerning the spring-tails is the manner in
which they find their way into the termite mounds. They cannot
travel far and they die in a few hours when exposed to the open
air. This particular species has, in fact, never been found anywhere but inside termite nests. When once established in a
termitary they never leave it but breed and die there, generation after generation. But how does the infestation start? How
do the first spring-tails get into a nest? We don't know. It may
be that the flying termites, when they leave home on their
nuptial flight, carry with them a few spring-tail eggs adhering
to their bodies—but this is pure speculation, although it does
seem to be a likely explanation of the manner in which the
little creatures spread with their hosts.

Another tiny creature that has found the sheltered, damp
darkness of the termitary well suited to its needs is the white
mite, *Termitacarus cuneiformis*. Oval in shape, about half a
millimetre, or one-fiftieth of an inch in length, white or very
pale yellow, with a prominent spine at the hind end of the
body, this mite is very common in the nests of many kinds of
termites found in Africa. It can be seen riding on the backs of
workers and soldiers, but it is most frequently found on the
queens (Plate Vb). It is very active and runs over the backs of
the termites, often leaping from one to another like a miniature
circus-rider. When a worker is feeding another or is attending
to the queen, mouth to mouth, then the mite will run down and
steal a little of the food as it passes between them. The mites
may be found in almost every nest that is examined, but they
are never very numerous and they seem to do no harm. They

are tolerated by the termites, which make no apparent effort to get rid of them.

These white mites belong to the large family known as the *Gamasidæ*, the members of which show a great diversity of habits. Many are free living and feed on vegetable matter, some of them being injurious to cultivated plants, whilst others feed on decaying vegetation. Quite a number of them are blood-suckers and live on rodents, bats and birds. The white mite, *Termitacarus cuneiformis*, is found only in termite nests and is widely spread in Africa.

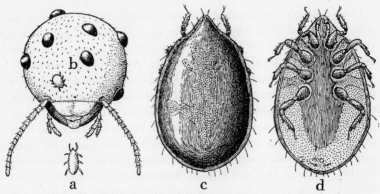

a                    c                    d

FIG. 27.—The Red Mite, *Cosmoglyphus kramerii*, that is common in the nests of termites: (*a*) young stage of the mite, (*b*) the resting stage, or hypopi, adhering to the head of a worker termite, (*c*) adult mite viewed from above, (*d*) the same viewed from below. The full-grown mite is about one-fortieth of an inch long.

Frequently, when a mound is broken open, termites may be seen with small, hemispherical, red excrescences on their heads and other parts of the body, each about a quarter of a millimetre in diameter. They may be found at any time of the year but are commonest in the autumn. Sooner or later they appeared in all my nests and, in some cases, they became so numerous that they covered almost completely the heads of workers and soldiers and were thickly dotted over their bodies. These are the resting stage of the red mite, *Cosmoglyphus kramerii*, and they are using the termites as a means of transport. They do no harm unless they become so numerous as to impede the movements of their hosts (Plate VIIIa).

This mite belongs to another large family, the *Tyroglyphidæ*, which includes many species that are common in houses, on food-stuffs such as flour, cheese and bran, and other species that sometimes appear in large numbers on furniture that is stuffed with feathers or animal and vegetable fibres. A number of species are found in damp places, where they feed on dead and decaying animal and vegetable matter. Like all other mites, they have four stages in their life history, the egg that hatches into a six-legged larva, this moults to an eight-legged stage called the first nymph, which gives rise to a second nymph, also eight-legged, and this finally develops into the adult mite. Many species of Tyroglyphid mites have an extra stage, a resting period called the hypopus, between the first and second nymphal stages, and it is these dormant mites that are seen on the bodies of the termites. This is a provision to enable the little creatures to survive under adverse conditions and to spread from place to place. When it is ready to change into a hypopus the nymph fastens itself in position by means of a sucker on the underside of its body, just behind the bases of the hind legs, and it becomes motionless and takes no food, remaining like this for weeks if necessary, until more favourable conditions return, when it moults into the second nymphal stage and becomes active once more.

Inside the termitary, the young Tyroglyphid mites can be seen as tiny oval specks, just visible to the naked eye, running actively about in the cells. They are almost certainly scavengers and feed on such edible debris as they can find. At this stage they have only six legs, but they moult to the first nymphal stage and take on a more rounded form and have an extra pair of legs. They continue to feed and grow until they are nearly half a millimetre long and have rounded, shiny backs, but are still white. Then, when they are ready to enter upon the resting stage, they creep on to the termites and, as a rule, make their way on to the heads. Here they settle down, fastening themselves securely in position by means of their suckers and in a day or so they assume a deep red colour. They remain like this for two or three weeks, and it may be longer.

Adult red mites have been found in decaying vegetable matter away from the termite mounds and these may have arisen from hypopi that have dropped off the workers when out foraging for food. The majority of the hypopi, however, drop off inside the nest and become second-stage nymphs that look something like miniature, smooth-backed red tortoises. They feed on anything they can find that is edible and, in nests where the mortality among the termites has been too great for the workers to deal with the corpses, I find them clustered on the dead bodies and obviously feeding on them. Later on they turn into adults, which are similar to the second-stage nymphs but have harder backs and are of a darker red colour. Winged termites, waiting for the nuptial flight in the autumn, may often be seen with hypopi on their heads and bodies and it is clear that the mites can be carried to new nests in this way. Hence it is not surprising that they are common and widely spread.

It is quite easy to dig up the mounds of the black-mound termite on the veld and to turn them over in order to see what is underneath. This can be done with the help of a spade, or even a stout walking-stick can be thrust into the soil at the side of a mound and used as a lever; a small termitary can be up-rooted by hand. When a mound is turned over in this way, some curious grubs may often be seen beneath it. They are dirty grey in colour, about an inch long and lie coiled up on their side in the shape of the letter "C". They lie quite still when exposed, with the head bent down and tucked well into the belly. As they are always coated with dirt of the same colour as the soil beneath the mound, they are not easy to find, despite their size. If you are patient and wait and watch, you will see these fat grubs uncoil after a time and try to make their escape by creeping away on their backs. Although they have six perfectly good legs, they never attempt to use them for walking in the ordinary way. Instead, they turn wrong side up, with their legs in the air, and muscular contractions pass along the body from the front rearwards; the short, stiff bristles on the back catch in the roughnesses of the ground and they are propelled forward in this unorthodox fashion at quite a good speed.

The grubs bury themselves quickly enough in the soft soil if they are given the opportunity. If one of these creatures is caught and the dirt washed off its body, it will be seen that its real hue is a dirty white and that its body is clothed in short, stiff bristles to which the particles of soil adhere. Along each side it has nine conspicuous brown dots that mark its nine pairs of breathing holes, or spiracles. Like many other insects, it has a pair of spiracles on the first segment of the thorax, immediately behind the head, none on the second and third thoracic segments, and then a pair on each of the eight succeeding abdominal segments. Its head is hard and dark brown and it is armed

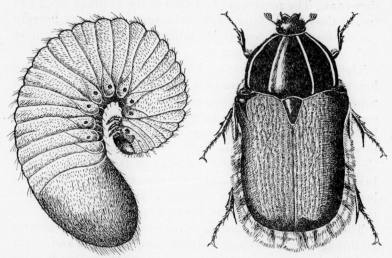

Fig. 28.—The Green Protea Beetle, *Trichostetha fascicularis*. Adult on the right, larva on the left. The larva lives as a scavenger beneath the mounds of the black-mound termite. The beetle is green and black, with tufts of pale brown hairs on its abdomen. It is about an inch and a quarter long.

with a pair of powerful mandibles that are well able to deal with tough food material.

The grubs burrow in the soil and loose material at the base of the mound and live on such organic matter as they can find there. They excavate cavities in the bottom of the mound itself and swallow the particles impregnated with the excreta of the termites. Rains beating down on the mounds carry organic matter into the soil beneath and this also provides the grey larvæ with nourishment. In short, their chief, if not their only food, consists of termite droppings.

The larvæ grow slowly and they take eighteen months to reach full size. About the middle of the summer of the second year of their existence they construct neat, oval cells out of soil particles bound together with saliva and, inside these snug retreats underneath the termite mounds, they change into pupæ. The pupæ are beautiful objects, white and translucent, and they look as though they had been carved out of crystal; they are very different from the ugly grey grubs from which they came. The pupæ may be found in their cells in April and two or three weeks later, after the autumn rains have brought out the first protea flowers, the adult beetles emerge and make their way up into the open air.

The green protea beetle, *Trichostetha fascicularis*, is a very handsome insect, about an inch and a quarter long, with green wing-covers, black thorax marked with four white stripes, and a conspicuous fringe of pale brown hairs round the sides of its body (Plate XIVb). The antennæ are short and end in small, three-bladed fans which the beetle can open, as though it were sniffing the air, but usually it carries its feelers tucked away beneath its head. Hidden under the wing-covers it has a pair of brown, membranous wings and it is a strong flier, revelling in the sunshine and flying from protea to protea.

The beetles can be found inside the flower-heads of the proteas all through the winter and spring, feeding on pollen and nectar and playing an important part in the pollination of these beautiful plants that are such a characteristic feature of the flora of the Cape. Their jaws, unlike those of the larvæ, are soft and membranous and adapted for lapping up liquids. They belong to the group of striking, handsome beetles known as the *Cetoninæ*, a sub-family of the huge family, *Scarabæidæ*, that includes the well-known dung beetles and chafers and that is widely spread over the world. Like so many of its kind, the green protea beetle has a life history of strange contrasts—eighteen months or so spent in the soil feeding on excrement, followed by a few weeks of philandering in the sunshine, sipping at nectar and nibbling at pollen. A smaller relative, the speckled brown protea beetle, *Trichostetha capensis*, has a similar life history.

When a termitary of the black-mound termite is broken open,

PLATE XI

(*a*) The larva of the guest fly, *Termitometopia skaifei*, with adult
workers in attendance

The larva is about half an inch long and is only found in the nests during
the summer

(*b*) The guest fly, *Termitometopia skaifei*, just after it has emerged
from the puparium

The bladder that it uses in breaking out of the puparium can be seen
projecting from its head. After this is withdrawn the wings expand.

PLATE XII

(*a*) Observation nest for termites

Cork-lino nest on the right, feeding chamber on the left

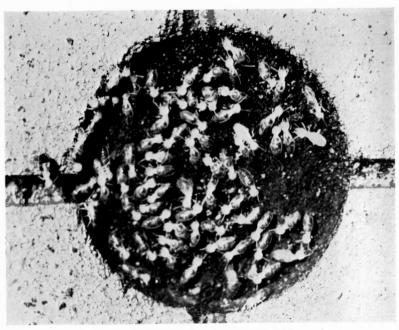

(*b*) One of the cells in the above nest, with workers

The cell is one and a quarter inches in diameter. The floor of the cell is covered with mound material.

one sometimes comes across a strange-looking creature, about three-quarters of an inch long, brown in colour and very hairy. It is usually found in one of the cells on the outside of the nest, near the base, and it quickly runs away and hides itself when it is exposed to the light. Although it appears to have ten legs, the long front pair are not legs at all, but feelers, or pedipalps, as they are called. They correspond to the pair of feelers seen on the front of the head of a spider, but they are much longer and they are held stretched out in front as the creature runs along: they are not used at all as legs in walking and running.

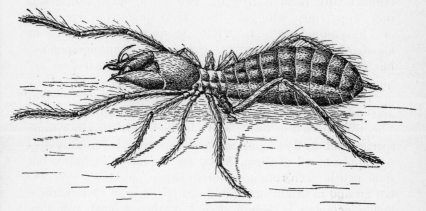

Fig. 29.—The Small Brown Jerrymunglum that preys on termites. It is about three-quarters of an inch long when fully grown and brown in colour.

The four pairs of limbs behind the pedipalps are the true legs, the first two pairs being small and weaker than the last two.

On top of the head there is a dark spot in the middle of which two simple eyes are lodged. The creature has very poor sight indeed and can do little more than distinguish light from darkness, but those two long pedipalps, covered with hairs, and the hairs that coat the body and legs are very sensitive and tell the hideous creature much about its surroundings. In a small hollow at the tip of each pedipalp there is a curious little bladder that can be protruded at will and that serves as an olfactory organ; in other words, this creature has its nose on the tip of its feelers. It has a pair of powerful jaws, like pincers,

7

projecting from the front of the head and it can administer
a sharp nip with these, but it has no poison glands.

There are comparatively few creatures in nature that are
really ugly, but it must be admitted that the *Solifugæ*, the
group to which this creature belongs, have little to recommend
them. Their ways are as unpleasant as their appearance.
About two hundred species are known from the warmer parts
of the world and only one or two of the smaller kinds penetrate
as far north as Greece and Spain in Europe. Larger ones are
common in Egypt and the Near East and troops became
familiar with these during the two world wars and it was
they, apparently, who gave them their quaint but apt name
of "jerrymunglums". In South Africa they are known as
*haarskeerders* (hair-cutters), or *jagspinnekoppe* (hunting spiders),
but neither of these names is suitable because their jaws are
quite incapable of cutting hair and they are not spiders. They
are relatives of spiders and scorpions but form a more ancient
and primitive group. The scientific name, *Solifugæ*, means
"fugitives from the sun", and although this describes some
species, such as that found in termite mounds, it certainly does
not apply to all of them. Many are nocturnal in habit, but
some can be seen running like miniature racehorses over the
hot ground in bright sunlight. Some of the large species, three
inches or more in length, found in the tropical and sub-
tropical parts of Africa, are capable of killing young mice and
shrews. On one occasion, in Bechuanaland, I came upon one
of them running down the wall of a hut at night with a dead bat
in its jaws. None of them is venomous, however, although the
large ones can inflict a painful bite. They are incorrigible
cannibals and, if two are placed in a box together, they invariably fight and the victor devours the vanquished.

The small species found living in or near the base of the
nests of the black-mound termite does not seem yet to have
been given a scientific name, so we must be content to call it
the small brown jerrymunglum of the Cape. It feeds on the
termites, breaking into their subterranean tunnels and crushing
its victims to pulp in its jaws. In my observation nests its
appetite seems to be insatiable and it destroys large numbers
of the defenceless insects. From time to time I see a jerrymun-

glum lying motionless in a cell it has excavated for itself in the sand beside the mound, with its legs folded stiffly over its back, and no amount of prodding will make it move. Probably it assumes this dormant phase when it is about to moult, but I am not sure on this point as I have never seen the process. In a few days the creature is running about again as hungry as ever. I know nothing about the breeding habits as I have not succeeded in getting a pair of them to settle down together; one has always eaten the other. The male has an extraordinary yellow knob on the top of each of his jaws, with a long, curved spike in front of it. Judging from observations made on other species of jerrymunglums, these curious ornaments on the head of the male are used in mating. On the underside of each hind leg, at the base, there are five flat, paddle-shaped appendages that serve some function or other, but it is not known what.

Insects that live in the abodes of others, but that are not parasites, are called inquilines. There is an inquiline termite that is common at the Cape and that is only found living in the nests of other species of termites; it never builds a home of its own. It has no common name and is known to science as *Termes winifredæ*; we will speak of it here as the inquiline termite. The colonies of this species are never large, consisting only of a few hundred individuals at most. About two per cent. of the termitaries of the black-mound termite contain colonies of these intruders, lodged in a few cells generally near the outside of the mound. The inquiline workers are similar in appearance to those of the black-mound termite, so much so that it is impossible to tell them one from the other by the naked eye, but the soldiers are quite different and easily recognised by their grotesque jaws. These are as long as the head, slender and only slightly curved, and they are generally held crossed one over the other.

Such a pair of jaws are useless for feeding or biting and, as a matter of fact, the soldiers fall easy victims to the soldiers and workers of the black-mound termite when they are attacked. They don't use their jaws for biting at all, but snap them open so as to strike their foes a sharp, sideways blow with them. Their method of using their jaws can be seen if one of them is teased with a grass stalk; the jaws suddenly jerk open and, if one of them strikes against the wall of a cell or against the ground, the soldier will be flung to one side, head over heels by the force of the blow. If those snapping jaws strike a soft-bodied foe then that insect is generally crippled and put out of the fight.

As soon as a mound containing these termites is broken open, they are attacked and killed by the rightful owners of the nest. They only survive in their lodgings by keeping the cells they occupy cut off from the rest of the mound and they have their

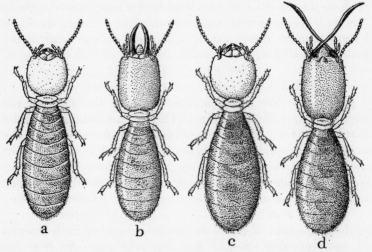

a        b        c        d

Fig. 30.—The Malmesbury Termite, *Microcerotermes malmesburyi*, (a) worker, (b) soldier.
The Inquiline Termite, *Termes winifredæ*, (c) worker, (d) soldier.

own runways leading down into the soil. The time of their nuptial flight also differs from that of the black-mound termite; you find winged inquilines in the nests during December, much earlier in the year than they appear among their host species. The king and queen of the inquilines are similar in appearance to those of the black-mound termite, but the queen is slightly smaller, more slender and pale yellowish brown in colour. It is strange that this particular species never attempts to construct a home of its own for it often pays very dearly for living, un-invited, in the home of deadly enemies.

Another termite that is frequently found living in the

mounds of the black-mound termite, but that is not a true
inquiline, is the Malmesbury termite, *Microcerotermes malmesburyi* (Plate IXb). This species builds nests of its own, but they
are difficult to find because they are completely buried in the
ground; there is no mound above the surface. The termitary of
the Malmesbury termite is a hard, brown cellular structure,
more or less cone-shaped, with the pointed end downwards
and the flat upper end just level with the ground surface. It is
generally only some six to nine inches long by four or five inches
wide. Often it is hidden under a stone, but sometimes the top of
a termitary may be seen at the surface where the soil has been
blown or washed away.

This species has habits similar to those of the black-mound
termite, but it feeds more on partially decayed wood and may
often be found burrowing in old protea stumps. The nuptial
flight takes place in April, usually in the afternoon, and it
would seem that the mated couples frequently find their way
into or beneath the termitaries of the black-mound termite and
make their home there. They avoid all contact with the owners
of the mound, otherwise they would be killed at once, and they
make their own nest inside the precincts of the well-protected
fortress, as a separate entity.

As time passes the nest of the Malmesbury termite becomes
completely enclosed in the more rapidly growing termitary of
its host and the two form a compound whole. But the two
species never mingle. They have their own separate runways
and often the Malmesbury termite will build covered thoroughfares running down over the surface of the mound to reach the
ground. If a compound nest is broken open and the two species
are thrown together, they at once join in combat, workers and
nymphs joining the soldiers in the fight, and the struggle only
ends when all on one side or the other have been killed.

This species receives its name from the fact that it was first
discovered near the little town of Malmesbury, in the wheat
district about fifty miles from Cape Town, but it is widely
spread throughout the south-western Cape. The workers are
small, being only about three millimetres long, and are reddish
brown, and the soldiers have more or less rectangular, yellow
heads armed with comparatively small, simple jaws.

## Chapter Twelve

# A STRANGE PARTNERSHIP

IF dead stumps of proteas and other trees and bushes on the mountain slopes of the south-west Cape are split open, colonies of an interesting primitive termite may be found in some of them. This is the flat-headed termite, *Porotermes planiceps*, and it makes its home entirely in dead wood, close to the surface of the ground or just below it. The nest consists of flattened cells eaten out of the softer parts of the wood and running with the grain, the chambers being connected one with the other by narrow corridors. These termites make their home and obtain their food at the same time by hollowing out the edible portions of the wood; they do not enter the soil at all.

The colonies are small, the largest of them consisting only of two or three hundred individuals and most of them being smaller than this. There are no workers in the nest as there is so little work to be done that it appears they are not needed, and their place is taken by the nymphs that will eventually develop into flying termites, destined to leave the nest and go out and establish new colonies elsewhere. Just before they are fully grown, and before their wings have expanded, these nymphs do such work as is required, such as feeding and caring for the young and the queen and feeding the soldiers. The soldiers are easily recognised by their large, flat heads and powerful jaws. They are about half an inch long, pale yellow in colour and there are generally only half a dozen or so of them in a moderate-sized colony. Their legs are stout and at the apex of each tibia there are three spines, those on the hind tibiæ being arranged in the form of a triangle; this is the character that enables one to distinguish this species from all others. Only three species of this genus, *Porotermes*, are known in the world, one from Australia, a second from Chile and the third is the South African species we are now considering.

This species is mentioned here in order to introduce the

extraordinary parasites that are found in the gut of primitive termites, but not in the higher members of the group, the *Termitidæ*. If a soldier or large nymph of the flat-headed termite is dissected and the gut contents examined under the microscope an amazing sight is revealed. No great skill is required to carry out such a dissection. The termite is killed and placed in a drop of water or normal saline solution on a microscope slide and then two needles are taken and one is

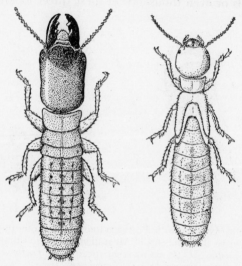

Fig. 31.—The Flat-headed Termite, *Porotermes planiceps*. Soldier on the left, nymph that serves as a worker on the right. The soldier is about half an inch long.

stuck into the insect's head and the other into the abdomen, as near the hind end as possible. The two needles are now pulled gently and steadily apart and, with a little luck and patience, the head of the termite comes away, bringing the whole of the alimentary canal attached to it. There are three pouches in the hind intestine, filled with semi-liquid material, and if these are crushed and examined, the contents will be seen to consist of fragments of partially digested food, together with an enormous number of strange parasites. They swarm to such an extent in these large intestinal pouches that it is estimated they make up nearly one-third of the termite's total weight, and most of them are comparatively large so that they are easily visible under the low power of the microscope and the largest of them can even be seen with the naked eye, as tiny white specks. They are minute animals, protozoa, and the great majority of them are flagellates, so called because they have long filaments on their bodies called flagella that lash to and fro and propel the little creatures through the liquid in which they live.

Hundreds or even thousands of these queer-looking protozoa

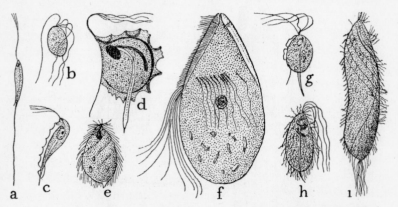

FIG. 32.—Some of the Parasitic Protozoa found in the intestines of Termites. All drawn to the same scale. Magnified about 200 times: (*a*) *Tricer-comitus termopsis*, (*b*) *Monocercomonas* species, (*c*) *Trichomonas trypanoides*, (*d*) *Trichomonas termopsidis*, (*e*) *Spironympha porteri*, (*f*) *Trichonympha campanula*, (*g*) *Trichomonas lighti*, (*h*) *Metadevescovina debilis*, (*i*) *Di-nenympha fimbriata*. (After Kirby.)

may be seen moving about amid the partially digested food, squirming and writhing and jostling one another in a dense throng, so closely packed that they have scarcely room to move. It is a fantastic zoological and botanical garden in miniature for, besides the protozoa, there are innumerable bacteria and spirochætes, much smaller than the animal parasites and more difficult to see. The largest and commonest of the protozoa are known as Trichonymphids and have several long flagella on them which they must have difficulty in using in their over-crowded environment. Some of them appear to have short, curly hairs attached to their bodies (Figure 32 h and i), but these are really spirochætes adhering to them, and they are probably parasitic upon the parasites. In fact, some half a dozen different kinds of lesser parasites have been found on the protozoa that infest termites.

Tiny particles of food can be seen embedded in the semi-transparent bodies of the Trichonymphids and it is obvious that they feed on the contents of the alimentary canal of their host. Other kinds of protozoa show no such solid inclusions and it seems that they feed on dissolved organic matter in the liquid of the gut, whilst still others feed on bacteria and smaller protozoa. Those large intestinal pouches of the primitive termite are queer, self-contained worlds teeming with incredible inhabitants, seething, struggling, multiplying, eating and being eaten.

Each group of primitive termites has certain types of protozoa associated with it and scientists who have made a special study of them can tell, from an examination of the parasites, what kind of termite they came from. They may even be used as an aid in the classification of termites because it is considered that species with similar parasites are more closely related than those that have dissimilar ones. Cockroaches also have these intestinal protozoa, but to a much less extent than the termites.

How do the termites become infected and how do the parasites spread throughout the colony until all the members, except the young, contain them? No cysts have been found in the case of the flagellate protozoa and, without such resistant forms, they cannot exist in the open, therefore they must pass directly from one insect to another. This is done by the termites unpleasant habit of feeding on one another's excrement. When a termite casts its skin it loses the contents of its intestine because the lining of this part of the body is discarded with the rest of the skin, and it loses the parasites at the same time. But it is soon reinfected after the moult by its insanitary method of feeding. A young king and queen carry the parasites with them when they leave their home to go out and establish a new colony elsewhere, and later on their offspring become infected from them. So the close association between the termites and their peculiar protozoa has gone on through the ages and neither can exist without the other.

So far the protozoa have been spoken of as parasites, but are they really parasites? May they not be symbionts or commensals? A parasite is a creature that lives at the expense of its host and harms it; a commensal is one that lives with another and may or may not benefit from the association, but neither suffers injury from the presence of the other; symbionts are creatures that live together to their mutual advantage. The general consensus of opinion today is that certain of the protozoa found in the gut of the lower termites are symbionts, whilst others are commensals and some are parasites. The principal constituent of the food of wood-inhabiting termites is cellulose and this is a substance that is very difficult to digest and few animals are able to deal with it. Certain protozoa and bacteria can digest cellulose, however, and these are the symbionts that are essential for the well-being of their hosts.

By a series of striking experiments carried out about twenty-five years ago at Harvard University, Dr. L. R. Cleveland showed that the protozoa in the gut could be killed, but the termites not injured, if they are kept at a temperature of thirty-six degrees Centigrade for twenty-four hours, or if the insects are starved for some time, or, most successful method of all, if they are kept in an atmosphere of almost pure oxygen at a pressure of fifty or sixty pounds to the square inch for half an hour or so. When the micro-organisms in the gut are destroyed in this way the termites die in two or three weeks when fed on filter paper, which contains nothing but cellulose, whereas they can live for a much longer period on this diet if they have the symbiotic protozoa in their intestines. By clever manipulations of these experiments, Cleveland showed that it is possible to kill off some kinds of protozoa and leave others unharmed, and in this way he demonstrated that it is the Trichonymphids among the protozoa (Figure 32 f) that are the important ones in breaking down the cellulose and making it available to their hosts. The others seem to be mostly parasites or harmless commensals.

All this is very interesting and important, but it only applies to about one-quarter of all the known species of termites. The other three-quarters, belonging to the large family of higher termites, the *Termitidæ*, do not harbour the useful, symbiotic protozoa. If an adult worker of the black-mound termite is dissected in the manner briefly described at the beginning of this chapter, and if the alimentary canal is examined, it will be seen to consist of the following parts. The front part, leading from the mouth, is a slender, thin-walled colourless

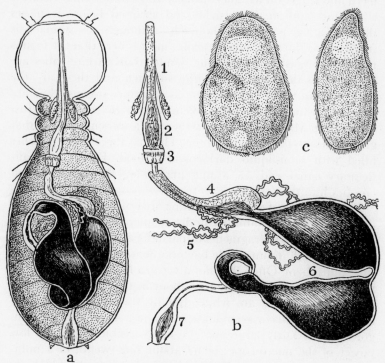

FIG. 33.—The Alimentary Canal of the Black-Mound Termite and its curious parasite: (*a*) the alimentary canal in position in a worker's body ; (*b*) the gut removed and uncoiled, (1) the œsophagus and salivary glands, (2) crop, (3) gizzard, (4) stomach, (5) Malpighian tubes, (6) the pouches of the intestine, (7) rectum ; (*c*) the parasite, *Nyctotherus silvestrianus*, as seen from above on the left, side view on the right—drawn from living specimens.

tube, the pharynx and the œsophagus, with the salivary glands on either side. At the rear end this tube is somewhat distended to form the crop. The food, after it is swallowed and mixed with salivary juices, passes along this tube into the crop by means of muscular contractions and its passage must be rapid, for little or no food is found in this part of the canal when a termite is dissected.

The crop is followed by a small, thick-walled chamber called the gizzard, which has a complicated arrangement of chitinous teeth and ridges on its inner surface, and it is here that the food is ground into small particles and strained before it passes through a valve into the stomach. Although the stomach is small, it has thick, glandular walls and it is here that the food is mixed with gastric juice. Four slender, curly white tubes are attached to the hind end of the stomach and these are the Malphighian tubes that function as excretory organs; they are long and wind in a tangled skein among the intestines. Just behind the Malphighian tubes there is a muscular valve that gives access to the bulky intestine. This has three large pouches filled with semi-liquid dark-coloured food. Finally, the alimentary canal ends in a muscular tube, the colon, which empties into the rectum.

If the pouches of the hind intestine are crushed on a glass slide and the contents examined under a microscope, they will be found to consist of fragments of partially digested food, brown in colour, with innumerable bacteria floating in the liquid that surrounds them. Often, but not always, a few peculiar parasites will be seen swimming actively about in the film of liquid. By reflected light they are white, but by transmitted light they are grey and have a granular appearance. As micro-organisms go, they are fairly large and are easily visible under the low power of the microscope, being about one-twelfth of a millimetre, or one three-hundredth of an inch in length. The body of the parasite is covered with microscopic filaments, cilia, as they are called, which lash to and fro and propel it through the water. As one watches a living specimen moving about, its body appears to be surrounded by what look like a miniature heat haze, due to the movement of the cilia; when it slows down the cilia look like a tiny field of wheat lashed by the wind.

The protozoon is egg-shaped and it swims with the small end forwards. Occasionally it rolls over on its side and then it can be seen that the front end is flattened and more or less pointed. Near the front end there is a large oval spot that is paler than the rest of the body in a fresh specimen; this is the macronucleus. On one side is what might well be described as a mouth and gullet, a cone-shaped indentation that leads to the interior of the body and that is lined with long cilia that wave constantly to and fro. Every two or three minutes a circular pale spot appears and disappears at the hind end of the body; this is the contractile vacuole and is the creature's means of ridding itself of waste matter; it opens into a tiny pore at the rear end which serves as an anus. Thus, although it is only a lowly one-celled animal, this protozoon has a complicated structure.

In pure water on the microscope slide the parasites die quickly, within five minutes or so, but they survive longer in normal saline solution. In water they soon come to a stop and swell and then disintegrate, due to the absorption of water; the same thing happens in the salt solution, but it takes longer. Occasionally an individual may be seen that is in the process of dividing into two. A constriction appears across the middle of the body, the macronucleus divides into two, one half moving towards the hind end of the body, and a new mouth and gullet are formed here. Then the two halves separate and each goes its own way. This is the parasite's normal way of multiplying.

Less frequently parasites may be seen that are smaller than the others, quite motionless, without any cilia and enclosed in a thick, transparent membrane. These are encysted individuals that are in a resting stage, able to withstand unfavourable conditions. They do not disintegrate on the microscope slide and they are probably in a resistant state, able to survive if passed out to the exterior.

These protozoa are by no means numerous. Usually only half a dozen or so are found in the gut of a worker or soldier, and often they are absent altogether. Much depends upon the colony from which the insects are taken; in some colonies nearly all the soldiers and workers are infected, whilst in others the parasites are very few and far between. They are not found in young termites. They do not seem to harm their hosts in any way. As these parasites have a mouth and gullet, it would seem that they feed on solid particles, probably on bacteria and partially digested food in the termite's intestine. Living in sheltered conditions amid a super-abundance of food, it is strange that they do not multiply enormously and swarm in those large, intestinal pouches, but this they never do, and there must be some reason for it about which we know nothing.

The parasite is known to science as *Nyctotherus silvestrianus*, and it has only been found in termites belonging to the same genus as the black-mound termite, *Amitermes*. It was first described and named in 1932 by the late Dr. H. Kirby from termites of this group found in California, and so far it has not been recorded from any other species. That termites closely related but separated so far apart geographically as the Cape and California should harbour the same species of parasite is remarkable and would indicate that the association between these insects and their parasites has been of very long duration. Other species of *Nyctotherus* have been recorded from cockroaches, centipedes, fish and frogs.

It will be seen, then, that the protozoa found in the gut of higher termites, such as *Amitermes*, are very different from those that swarm in the intestines of the lower, wood-infesting termites. They are so few in numbers that they cannot play any important part in the digestion of their hosts and are probably parasites that do little harm.

## Chapter Thirteen

# THE CASTE PROBLEM

ACCORDING to the dictionary, a "caste" is one of the hereditary classes into which society is divided in India, or it is a social class based on artificial grounds. But the entomologist uses the word in a different sense. He speaks of the castes found in the beehive, ants' nest and termite mound, and by that he means the distinct types of workers, soldiers and kings and queens found among social insects.

There are five castes in the nests of the black-mound termite —workers, soldiers, primary, secondary and tertiary reproductives. As a general rule, only three of these castes are found in any one nest; usually only one type of reproductive is present with the workers and soldiers. These castes differ from one another profoundly in ways that have already been described, and the problem of their origin has been hotly debated by entomologists for many years, but so far no satisfactory answer has been found.

Briefly, the problem may be stated as follows: Does the termite queen lay different types of eggs, eggs that develop into workers, others that develop into soldiers, and still others that give rise to sexual individuals we call kings and queens? In other words, are the castes determined by hereditary factors? Or does the queen lay only one type of egg and are the castes determined by environmental factors as the insects grow up? In other words, are the newly-hatched young all alike and do they change into workers, soldiers or reproductives as a result of differential treatment of some sort or other? Or is the development of the various castes due to a combination of hereditary and environmental factors?

Some students of termites believe in the first of these possibilities; they support what is known as the theory of intrinsic causes, or the blastogenic theory, and they assert that the queen

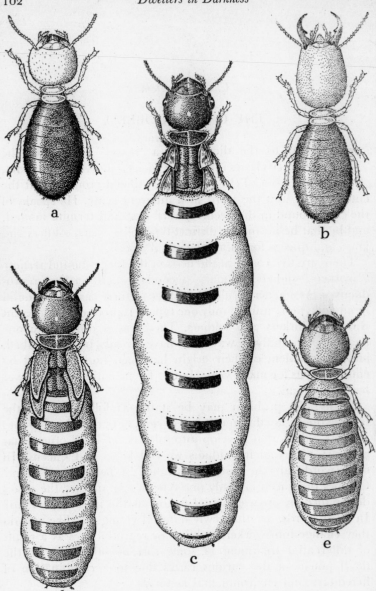

FIG. 34.—The Five Castes found in the Nests of the Black-Mound Termite. (*a*) worker, (*b*) soldier, (*c*) primary queen, (*d*) secondary queen, (*e*) tertiary queen. All drawn to the same scale.

PLATE XIII

(*a*) Nest with runways cut in plaster of Paris and a food-chamber
in each corner

The mound stands in a box of sand in the middle

(*b*) Observation nest for feeding experiments

There are six food-chambers in this particular model, three on each side.
The mound has been broken up for examination and the pieces, together
with the inhabitants, put in the box in the middle.

PLATE XIV

(*a*) The burrowing frog, *Breviceps rosei*

It never goes near water, blows itself up like a ball when alarmed and
feeds on termites and other insects

(*b*) The green protea beetle, *Trichostetha fascicularis*

As a larva it lives beneath the mounds of the black-mound termite, but
it spends its adult life amid protea flowers

lays worker-producing, soldier-producing and reproductive-producing eggs. Others stoutly maintain that the second explanation is the correct one, that the theory of extrinsic causes, or the trophogenic theory, gives the right answer; they are convinced that the young are all alike when they hatch and that the remarkable differences that appear in them as they develop are due to the varied treatment they receive. Some believe that a combination of these two alternatives is the only way in which the observed facts can be satisfactorily explained. The problem is a fascinating one and the correct solution, when it is found, may yield information that is of great interest and value.

Let us examine the evidence for and against these theories. Most observers are agreed that young termites, less than half grown, all look alike, that there are no visible differences to show whether they are going to develop into workers, soldiers, or reproductives. In order to confirm this, I have collected literally thousands of young termites from the territaries of the black-mound termite that I have broken up during the past fifteen years or so. These were collected at different times of the year and preserved in fifty per cent. alcohol for examination and comparison under the microscope. Each lot from a mound was kept separate and labelled with the date when taken; this is important, as will appear later.

It was found that all the young termites are alike until they are half grown, about 2·5 millimetres in length. They are all white, with soft, budlike mouthparts quite incapable of chewing solid food, and with no traces of wings or eyes. This might be taken as an indication that the theory of extrinsic causes is the correct one and that the queen lays only one type of egg, but this does not follow. For comparison with the black-mound termite I collected immature stages of the snouted harvester termite, *Trinervitermes gemellus* (Figure 12), and I found that the newly-hatched young of this species are so like those of the black-mound termite that it is impossible to separate them if they get mixed up. Yet the two species are very different and it is obvious that the young, although so similar in appearance, must come from very dissimilar eggs.

About forty years ago the Swiss entomologist, E. Bugnion,

8

who worked on the termites of Ceylon, published a drawing of a newly-hatched snouted termite of that island, *Nasutitermes lacustris*, purporting to show that the young soldier has the peculiar snout and frontal gland already well developed when it emerges from the egg. This drawing has been reproduced in later works and it is given again here (Figure 35) because it is important. If Bugnion is correct, then the various castes *are* differentiated in the eggs and the theory of intrinsic causes is established.

But Bugnion was wrong in his interpretation of what he saw when he examined his specimens under the microscope. In all young termites the labrum is a prominent lobe that juts out

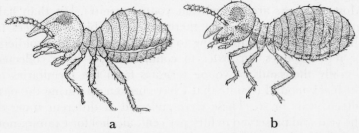

a                                                      b

FIG. 35.—Newly-hatched Termites: (*a*) the snouted termite of Ceylon, *Nasutitermes lacustris* (after Bugnion), (*b*) the snouted termite of the Cape, *Trinervitermes gemellus*. What Bugnion thought were the snout and the frontal gland are the labrum and the brain.

like a snout, and what he thought was the frontal gland was really the brain showing through the translucent wall of the head. The brain of a newly-hatched termite is comparatively much larger than it is in the adult; it occupies a large part of the cranium, whereas in the adult worker most of the head is filled with the strong muscles that work the jaws, whilst the brain, which scarcely increases in size as the insect grows, is much less conspicuous and is situated well forward near the bases of the antennæ.

An American student of termites, Miss C. B. Thompson, has published papers in which she claims to have found differences in young termites that distinguish the various castes. She describes one type with a large brain and sexual organs and an opaque body which, according to her, develops into the reproductive caste, and another type with small brain and sexual organs and a translucent body that gives rise to the sterile castes. But the differences she indicates are slight and ill-defined and her evidence is unconvincing. I found no such differences in the young of the black-mound termite or of the snouted harvester termite.

One fact emerged early in my investigations that has an important bearing on this problem. The queen of the black-mound termite begins to lay in September and the progeny that arise from these first eggs of the season are more than half grown by the end of November. Examination of immature individuals at this time of the year shows that all of them are developing into workers; there are no soldiers or reproductives among the first batch of young reared in the spring. It would seem, then, that the termites can control the appearance of the different castes in their nests. Early in the year, when more workers are needed for food-getting and brood-rearing, only workers are produced. Soldiers and winged individuals are only reared later in the year, after midsummer. Furthermore, in young and in weak colonies no white sexual nymphs are found at all, probably because their production is too big a drain upon the resources of such colonies.

If the castes are determined by hereditary factors carried in the eggs, then we should expect them to appear at all times throughout the breeding season, but this does not happen. If the queen lays different types of eggs, then the non-appearance of soldiers and sexual nymphs among the first brood of the year indicates that she can control her egg-laying and produce only the type of eggs required at the time. Such selective egg-laying on the part of the queen is highly improbable. Another explanation of the fact that the different castes appear only when needed may be that the workers devour the unwanted eggs and young. This would mean that they must be able to recognise the different types very early and that, in the spring, they destroy all but those destined to develop into workers. There is no evidence to support this point of view.

Investigations carried out at the University of California have shown that, among certain primitive wood-inhabiting termites found in that part of the world, there is also some degree of control over the appearance of the different castes in the nests. For example, in the case of the damp-wood termite, *Zootermopsis angusticollis*, the first brood of a young king and queen always includes one soldier, and one soldier only. There are no workers in the nests of these primitive termites; their place is taken by sexual nymphs; living as they do in the midst of their food and hollowing out their home as they eat, there is little work to be done, therefore the worker caste has either never arisen among them or it has disappeared. The first batch of young of the royal couple in a newly-established colony, then, consists of one soldier and some half a dozen nymphs. If the soldier is removed from such a nest, another appears within ten weeks or so, and this is repeated as often as a soldier is taken away. The queen must therefore be able to lay a soldier-producing egg if and when required and to withhold such eggs at other times, or the termites must be able to convert one of their number into a soldier whenever the need arises.

Young soldiers may be found in the nests of the black-mound termite from midsummer onwards. When they are a little more than half grown, between 2·5 and 3 millimetres long, some of the immature termites may be picked out that differ from the others in the shape of the head and the mandibles. The head is slightly longer than the width and the jaws are curved and have each one tooth on the inner edge; these are the marks of the soldier. The change in the shape of the mandibles appears suddenly. Among my specimens I have found several that were just about to moult and in these the curved sharp jaws, still soft and white, can be seen lying inside the broad, blunt mandibles of the previous instar. As the soldier grows its head elongates still more and the mandibles become slender and curved and they harden only in the penultimate instar. The workers, on the other hand, retain the round head and the broad mandibles with two or three marginal teeth on each; also their bodies assume a faint yellowish tinge when they are more than half grown, but this slight change of colour does not occur with the other castes.

After midsummer a third type may be seen among the half-grown young in a prosperous colony. These have small triangular outgrowths on each side of the second and third thoracic segments; they are young sexual individuals with their wings just beginning to show. Their heads and jaws are exactly like those of the workers. By the end of February they have grown to six millimetres in length, larger than the adult workers, and their wing-pads reach nearly two-thirds the length of the abdomen (Figure 17). Eyes appear at this stage, colourless at first, but they become pigmented and black just before the final moult. The rest of the body is pure white because these nymphs are fed all the time by the workers on predigested food. In February or early in March they cast their skin for the last time and become winged adults ready to go out on their nuptial flight after the first autumn rains.

Besides the long-winged white nymphs, there are nymphs with short wing-pads, reaching back only as far as the second segment of the abdomen, and of a greyish colour because they eat coarser food than the white nymphs (Plate VIIIa). These do not moult into the final stage but retain their short wing-pads and their half-developed eyes, it may be for many months, because they are to be found in the nests at any time of the year, whilst the long-winged nymphs are present only in the late summer. These are obviously sexual nymphs that have, for some reason or other, failed to mature, although they grow to the same size as the long-winged nymphs. It is probable that the nature of their food has something to do with this; they are not kept prisoners in the nest and fed by the workers, but go out foraging for food, something that their white, long-winged brothers and sisters never do.

My observations have convinced me that they are kept in reserve in case anything should happen to the king and queen, for it is these short-winged nymphs that are capable of developing into secondary reproductives. The flower-pot experiments, by means of which numbers of secondary kings and queens can be obtained, have already been described (see page 62). These secondaries appear only in the pots that contain some short-winged nymphs, together with a few thousand adult workers. If long-winged nymphs only are included with the workers, they develop normally into winged adults or are destroyed; they do not give rise to secondaries.

This leaves us with only the fifth caste, the tertiary kings and queens, to be accounted for. These are rare and they are more difficult to obtain experimentally than are the secondaries. They never appear in the flower-pots that contain adult workers and nymphs, and more often than not they fail to develop in the pots that contain workers and immature stages without nymphs; the young workers and soldiers simply grow up normally or they are killed and eaten by the adults. It seems that colonies with nymphs among the inhabitants cannot produce tertiary reproductives; they arise only in nests where no sexual nymphs are present because of the weakness of the colonies. In such weak communities immature workers may occasionally be seen that are larger than the others, about five millimetres long, as large as the adults, but their bodies are pale yellow because they are still being fed on predigested food by the adult workers. These are, I believe, immature workers that are similar to the short-winged nymphs in that they are in an arrested stage and are being kept in reserve in case of accident to the king and queen. They are found only in nests where there are no nymphs and where the old king and queen are failing and it is probable that they are individuals capable of developing into tertiaries should the need arise.

Should the reproductives in such a colony be lost, then these immature workers receive some form of treatment that causes their sexual organs to develop and become functional. It has been shown in the case of many insects that there is a connection between sexual maturity and the development of eyes and wings, and it is the same with the tertiary reproductives. The prothorax increases in size and at the same time small pointed outgrowths appear on the sides of the second and third thoracic segments, similar to those seen in young sexual nymphs when their wings begin to grow, and small, vestigial eyes appear on the head. The abdomen swells, that of the female more than that of the male, and the insects assume a yellow colour. These tertiaries are not much bigger than the adult workers and they run about actively in the nests and are difficult to find.

To sum up, it may be said that the observed facts can be most simply explained by assuming that all the newly-hatched young in a termite nest inherit the potentiality of growing up into winged, sexual adults, but only a few of them are allowed to develop fully and normally. Those that become workers are arrested at an early stage and retain most of the larval characters. The tertiary reproductives are also arrested at an early stage so that they retain most of the characters of the workers, but their sexual organs become functional and the vestiges of eyes and wings appear. The secondary reproductives are derived from nymphs of the primary form that have not been allowed to develop normally, so that they retain the wing-pads and imperfect eyes of the antepenultimate instar but become sexually mature. The soldiers, with their large heads and frontal glands and their jaws that differ so markedly from those of all other castes, are the most aberrant and the most difficult to account for; their bodies are like those of the workers, but their heads are profoundly modified.

We must now look for possible ways and means by which growth may be influenced so that the majority of the termites develop into workers, others into soldiers, and a comparative few into reproductives—and it is here that we meet with difficulties. It may well be that the stunted bodies and the sterility of the workers and soldiers are due to the lack of some form of nourishment that is essential to their full development, but we have no evidence of this. All the young are fed by the adult workers and they are all mixed up in the nest; there are no special cells or portions of the nest set aside for the various castes, as there are in the beehive, yet any differential feeding that goes on must be deliberate and purposeful so that each individual receives the correct treatment. If food is the only answer, then the termites must feed all their brood in the spring in such a way that they all grow into workers, whilst later in the year they select about five per cent. of their number for special treatment so that they develop into soldiers, and in prosperous colonies a comparative few are given a complete diet that causes them to become winged, sexual individuals.

If the castes are the result of differential feeding only, one would expect to find things going wrong occasionally in the nests and individuals being produced that are imperfect, that are intermediate between one caste and another. Such inter-castes, as they are called, have been found but they are rare and I have never seen any among the thousands of black-mound termites I have examined. Among certain species of termites in other parts of the world a few specimens of soldiers with

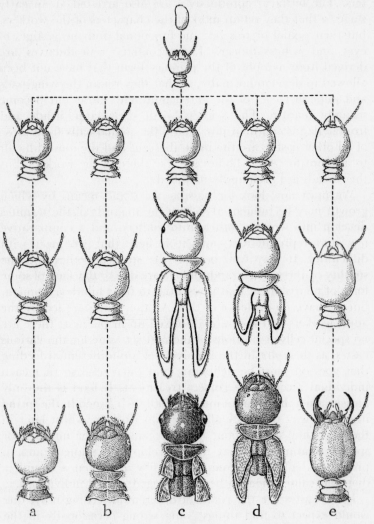

FIG. 36.—Caste Differentiation in the Black-Mound Termite: (a) development of worker, (b) of tertiary reproductive, (c) of primary reproductive, (d) of secondary reproductive, (e) of soldier. All the young appear to be alike until they are about half grown.

wing-pads on their backs and with functional sexual organs have been found, but as a general rule the distinctions between the castes are very clear cut and there are no intermediates such as one would expect if food alone were the cause of the differences. Nevertheless, the fertile soldiers and the soldiers with wing-pads do indicate that we are correct in assuming that all termites inherit the potentiality of developing into winged, sexual adults.

The workers of various species of termites are very similar to one another, but the soldiers differ greatly. If the large, oval yellow head and sharp, curved jaws of the black-mound soldier are due to special feeding, why does a like form of treatment produce a round, red head, a snout and minute jaws in the snouted soldiers of *Trinervitermes*? Why should the soldier of the inquiline termite have very long jaws for striking, whilst the Malmesbury soldier has short, sharp jaws for biting? The characters that distinguish the soldiers of the different species must be due to hereditary factors and we must assume that all young termites inherit them, so that the head and jaws characteristic of their species make their appearance if they receive the requisite treatment. In the individuals that develop into workers or reproductives, these soldier-characters remain dormant because the necessary stimulus for their appearance is lacking.

It is well known that termites lick and groom one another assiduously and it is assumed that they get in this way a fatty exudation, particularly from the abdomen of the queen, of which they are very fond. This led Holmgren about forty years ago to put forward what is known as the exudation theory. He assumed that all newly-hatched termites are alike, but some receive more food than others and consequently produce more of this fatty exudation. As a result they receive more attention and favourable treatment and they develop fully into the winged sexual forms. Those individuals that produce less exudation receive less food and attention and give rise to the sterile castes.

This theory has been elaborated by more modern investigators. Scientists at the University of California have put forward what is known as the inhibition theory. According to this, each caste secretes hormones that are given off in the fatty exudation and that tend to prevent the development of more members of the same caste in the nest. For example, the primary queen gives off a hormone that inhibits the development of any other females in the nest with functional sexual organs. As long as she is alive this hormone, obtained by the workers from her abdomen, circulates throughout the colony by communal feeding and prevents any other members from growing up into queens, but as soon as she is dead the inhibitory influence is removed and secondary or tertiary queens may appear. Similarly, if sufficient soldiers are present in a nest, the hormone given off by them tends to delay or prevent the development of more members of the same caste. In brief, the castes are determined by what has been called a balanced system of social hormones.

But there are serious objections to this theory. In the first place, if the king and queen give off powerful inhibitory hormones, why do winged males and females appear among their offspring, ready for the nuptial flight? Usually secondary kings and queens are found only in nests where there are no primary reproductives, but I have come across one nest of the black-mound termite in which there were several secondaries as well as the primary king and queen; in this case at least, the hormones from the primary pair failed to prevent the development of other reproductives. Also this theory of social hormones fails to account for the seasonal appearance of certain castes. Why do all the spring batch of young in the nest of the black-mound termite develop into workers? Why do long-winged white nymphs only make their appearance at midsummer and why do they fail to appear in weak or young colonies? Why does the first brood of a young king and queen of the damp-wood termite always consist of one soldier and the rest nymphs? It seems certain that a colony can control the development of the various castes, their time of appearance, their number and proportion, and the inhibition theory fails completely to explain this.

But we cannot dismiss the hormone theory as entirely wrong. Several glands have been found in insects that have been proved to produce hormones that exercise a profound influence on the growth and development. Perhaps the most important of these are two small glands associated with the brain, called the corpus allatum and the corpus cardiacum. These are found in practically all insects, including termites, and in their position and their far-reaching influence they remind one of the pituitary gland found in vertebrates. It has been proved experimentally that these glands secrete hormones that affect the growth, moulting and sexual maturity of insects. For example, removal of the glands from young silkworms causes them to pupate prematurely and in this way very small pupæ can be produced. On the other hand, if several glands, taken from other individuals of the same species, are implanted in young stick insects, they grow up into giants. By means such as these it has been shown that the corpus allatum produces what is called a juvenile hormone, a secretion that prevents the insect from maturing properly. As a result of all this work, it has been asserted that many of the abnormalities found among insects may be explained by assuming the production, too early or too late, in too high or too low a concentration, of the several hormones that regulate metamorphosis. It may well be the same with termites.

The corpus allatum of a termite queen undergoes an enormous increase in volume as she grows older, and it has also been shown that the same gland is larger in a soldier than it is in a worker, but in both these it is much smaller than that of the queen. It is the same with the corpus cardiacum. It is conceivable, therefore, that the hormones produced by the different castes vary in quantity and quality and that they control the differentiation. Over-production of the juvenile hormone might be the cause of the retention of larval characters by the workers, whilst the excessive growth and activity of the corpus allatum might account for the swollen abdomen and innumerable eggs of the queen.

In the present state of our knowledge, the observed facts are best explained by assuming that all young termites inherit the possibility of developing into any of the castes and that the insects themselves have some control over this development. The ancestral type is undoubtedly the winged individual, with compound eyes and functional sexual organs, and the other castes are derived from this by environmental and hereditary factors about which we know little or nothing. It may well be that the workers are stunted and sterile because of some lack in their diet; inside the beehive worker bees are produced in this way and the same may be true of termites. It is not so easy to account for the soldiers in this way. The head and jaws, differing so markedly from those of all the other castes, and showing such an amazing variety of form among the different species, must be due to genetic factors. To account for the appearance of soldiers in the nests only as and when required, and in the proportion desired, one must assume that the genes are present in all the eggs but that the soldier-characters only manifest themselves as the result of appropriate treatment.

Secondary reproductives are obviously modified forms of the primary; they are derived from nymphs that are prevented by some unknown means from reaching the adult state, but which become sexually mature. What little evidence we have concerning the tertiaries indicates that they arise from immature workers. If a weak colony that has no sexual nymphs in it loses its king and queen then some of the young workers may receive special treatment that causes their sexual organs to develop, and at the same time vestigial eyes appear on their heads and the rudiments of wings on their thoraces. In short, it seems that caste differentiation among termites is due to a combination of hereditary and environmental factors, that the theory of intrinsic and of extrinsic causes, the blastogenic and trophogenic theories both contribute to the answer. The termites can undoubtedly control the appearance of the various castes in the nest as the exigencies of the colony require and they do this by changes in environmental factors that bring about the appearance or suppression of the hereditary characters that distinguish the castes. We are still quite ignorant of the nature of these environmental factors by means of which the termites exercise control.

*Chapter Fourteen*

# THE SEAT OF AUTHORITY

ANOTHER fascinating problem that arises in the study of social insects is the question of control. How are order and discipline maintained? Who or what decides that this or that must be done? Is there any central authority and, if so, what form does it take? In our human communities we find an elaborate system of control is necessary, with an army, police force, judiciary, parliament, councils, managers, overseers and so on. Is anything comparable to be found in the beehive, ants' nest or termite mound? To us humans it seems inevitable that any crowded community must organise so that some are in authority and others must obey. A human city with many thousands of inhabitants, with every citizen on a footing of absolute equality and each going his or her own way, would soon be in a state of chaos, yet something like this seems to be the state of affairs inside a termite mound.

At first sight it might be thought that the soldiers act as a police force, but this is not so. They have so little control over the rest of the community that they are killed off and eaten if there are too many of them and they have to beg for the humblest of food. Their job is to guard the home from invasion and to protect the gangs of workers that go out foraging for food, and nothing more. The kings and queens are such in name only and they are certainly not the rulers of the state. Their sole function is to reproduce their kind and they are ruthlessly sacrificed if they fail in this. This leaves only the workers, and long study of these insects has convinced me that the adult workers are the real rulers and controllers of the community. Yet there are thousands of them and none, as far as we know, has any authority over the others.

When compared with other insects they are long-lived. I have kept workers alive in my observation nests for nearly two years, and in the natural state they may live much longer.

After watching them for many hours I have a strong suspicion that it is the oldest workers that are the leaders of the rest; that they initiate things and are blindly followed by all the others. Many attempts were made to colour individual workers with harmless dyes so that they could be recognised and their comings and goings watched, but all such attempts failed. They groom and clean one another so assiduously that any colouring matter sprayed on their bodies is quickly removed. Such dyes as methyl green, cochineal, trypan blue, azo black, and several others were used, squirted over the living insects until they were strongly coloured, but a few minutes later they were all as clean and indistinguishable as ever. I have fed them with foodstuffs coloured with these dyes, but there was no resulting change in the colour of their abdomens. Cellulose paint, including the coloured varnish that women put on their finger-nails, is the only thing I found that will stick to their bodies, but it seems to injure their delicate skin and they show signs of distress and, in any case, such marked individuals soon disappeared from my nests; either the paint was cleaned off by their fellows or they were killed and eaten. So far, then, I have failed to mark them so that I could follow the doings of individuals, as has been done with such success in modern studies of the honey bee.

Black-mound termites are nervous insects and when they are entering new territory the preliminary exploration is carried out slowly and cautiously by a few workers. For example, if a mound is placed on one of the stands described in the next chapter, the termites do not show themselves outside their home for some time, it may be for two or three days. Then a few workers venture into the food-chambers and these are soon followed by many others if they are left undisturbed. But if the first workers to enter the food-chambers are removed as soon as they show themselves, it may be a day or two before any more make their appearance. Furthermore, if these first venturesome workers are examined, they are found to have blunted teeth on their mandibles, and this is a sign of age; young adults have sharp teeth.

Sometimes in an artificial nest the termites will find a crack in the framework and they may try to find a way of escape across the table and down to the ground. As they never venture out into the open, they build black, covered runways of soil particles and excrement on the surface of the table. They are skilful and rapid tunnel-builders and the narrow corridors may extend three or four inches in a day, the insects never showing themselves while at work, but adding sticky particles through the tiny opening at the front end of the tunnel. When they reach the edge of the table they will drop their runway vertically down towards the ground, without any support except the edge of the table and they will continue this difficult engineering feat until their slender shaft reaches the ground, a black column not as thick as a lead pencil, yet strong enough to support its weight and the weight of numerous insects inside it over a distance of two or three feet, suspended in the air.

If the end of such a runway is broken down and the workers in it removed, then all further work on that tunnel ceases. Later on another runway may be started in a different direction, but if the process of removing the workers at the end is repeated, this also will be abandoned. After this has been done two or three times, all further attempts at escape cease, at least for some time, and I believe this is due to the fact that the older workers that pioneer this work have all been removed.

It is the workers that feed the queen and regulate her food supply so that she lays eggs as and when required. It is also the workers that kill the queen when her fertility is waning. They control and carry out the manifold activities of the community in the manner already described in this book, but it is a mystery how the various duties are allocated so that each task is performed as the need arises. For example, in some of my nests more of the insects die than can be devoured in the ordinary way and they become mouldy and are a threat to the health of the community. In such circumstances the excess corpses are walled off so that there is no further contact with them—in other words, an unusual emergency is met and dealt with adequately and in this, as in everything else, the community behaves as though it were under iron control. There are no strikes or forty-hour weeks in the termite mound.

The South African writer, Eugene Marais, in his book *The Soul of the White Ant*, and Maurice Maeterlinck in his *The Life of the White Ant*, both suggest that the termitary should be regarded as a single composite animal and not as a community of separate individuals. Marais goes so far as to write at length about what he called the "group soul" and to state that 'the termitary is a separate and composite animal in the same way that man is a separate composite animal' and that 'the termitary is an example of the method by which composite and highly developed animals like the mammals came into being.' He compares the surface of the mound with the skin, the cells and corridors with blood vessels, and the workers and soldiers with the corpuscles in these vessels, and the queen he regards as the equivalent of the brain. This is just nonsense and it does not help us to understand the organisation of the termite community at all. The inhabitants of the mound are just as much separate entities as are the inhabitants of a human city. If the termitary is "a separate and composite animal," then so is London and New York and Cape Town.

There is probably a division of labour inside the termitary as highly organised and strictly controlled as that found in the beehive, but we have so far no evidence of this, except the slight indications mentioned above. The use of the word "instinct" is rightly frowned upon by naturalists today because it explains so little. We are apt to say that the amazing ways of such insects as termites are instinctive, and to leave it at that. According to the dictionary, we mean by this that they are governed by innate propensities to certain seemingly rational acts performed without conscious design, and we are still left puzzled and wondering. Anybody who takes the trouble to study termites will come across many instances of what looks remarkably like intelligence and foresight on their part, and to say that they are creatures of instinct does not satisfy. Not the least of the mysteries surrounding them is the manner in which their complex communities are controlled, how the ruthless, iron discipline is maintained, why the individuals sacrifice themselves so readily and completely for the good of the community as a whole.

Maeterlinck sums up the conditions in the termitary as follows: 'All is darkness, underground tyranny, cruelty, sordid, filthy avarice, the atmosphere of the convict cell, of the penal settlement and the charnel house.' But in this statement he does them far less than justice. He is nearer the truth when he says: 'Their civilisation, which is the earliest of any, is the most curious, most complex, the most intelligent and, in a sense, the most logical, and best fitted to the difficulties of existence which has ever appeared before our own on the globe. From several points of view, this civilisation although fierce, sinister and often repulsive, is superior to that of the bee, of the ant, and even of man himself.'

*Chapter Fifteen*

# THE STUDY OF LIVING TERMITES

As was pointed out earlier in this book, termites are very delicate insects and difficult to keep alive in the laboratory. Certain primitive wood-inhabiting species that live in small colonies in dead timber have been studied extensively by keeping them in glass jars with pieces of wood, or by placing thin strips of wood between glass plates, but very few attempts have been made to keep nests of higher termites going in the laboratory. A simple type of artificial nest has been described consisting of a glass plate with strips of glass glued to it to form cells, but I have tried this and it did not prove successful, as the termites did not flourish in it, nor did they behave normally. I have also tried nests made of plaster of Paris, such as have been used for a long time in the study of ants, but these absorb too much moisture and they become contaminated and the termites mope and die in them.

After many failures I succeeded in devising a type of observation nest that proved satisfactory to myself and to the termites (Plate XIIa). This consists of a glass-bottomed tray with the nest in one half of it, and the other half serving as an outer chamber for food and exercise. The size of the tray is not critical; it depends upon the size of the colony one wishes to keep in it, but a useful size is twenty-four inches by eighteen inches, which is large enough to accommodate the inhabitants of a small mound about five inches high. A sheet of plate glass forms the base; this will not warp or absorb water and impurities. It is placed in a wooden tray with a rim one inch deep round the edge, to protect the glass from breakage and to make transport easy.

The nest itself consists of a piece of sheet cork, twelve inches by eighteen inches and a quarter of an inch thick. Rows of holes an inch and a quarter in diameter are punched in this cork and a sheet of the size mentioned will take seven rows with ten holes in each. The holes can be cut out with a sharp knife, but a punch makes a better and neater job. These holes form the cells in which the termites live and they are connected one with another by grooves an eighth of an inch deep and of the

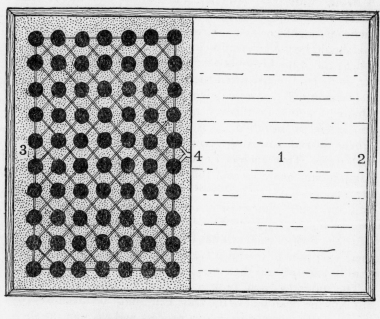

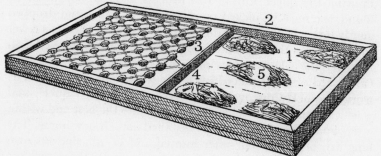

Fig. 37.—An Observation Nest for Termites. Plan above, side view below: (1) plate glass base, (2) wooden tray to hold glass base, (3) sheet cork with cells and grooves cut in it, (4) entrance to the nest, (5) heaps of food in the outside chamber. The whole tray is covered with a sheet of glass to maintain the necessary humidity of the air.

same width cut in the surface of the cork. The entrance to the nest consists of a wider groove cut in the middle of one of the longer sides of the cork sheet (Figure 37, 4).

The sheet of cork is now glued on one half of the glass base. A strong, waterproof adhesive is needed for this and I found plastic resin or plastic rubber suitable. A piece of glass, twelve inches by eighteen inches, forms the cover to the cork nest and this should be put in position on the nest when it is being glued down, and some heavy books placed on top so that it is quite flat and firmly fixed when the adhesive dries.

Termites will not settle down in a nest such as this unless it is "baited," and to do this you must first get hold of the mound you intend to install in it. A small portion of the mound is broken off and crushed to a powder and this is lightly moistened with water. Then each cell of the nest is nearly filled with the damp mound material and this is pressed down so as to form a firm, smooth floor to each cell; a small wooden cylinder, not quite one and a quarter inches in diameter and with a flat base, is a convenient implement for pressing the damp powder down. After the floor of each cell has been covered with material from their own mound in this way, the termites will enter the nest readily and take up their abode there.

The mound is now broken up and the inhabitants shaken out into the open half of the tray. Care must be taken to avoid injuring the queen during this process and, as soon as she is found, she must be picked up on a piece of paper and dropped gently into a cell in the middle of the cork nest. The glass cover is then put on the nest and finally a sheet of glass large enough to cover the whole tray is placed in position, and a piece of cardboard or cloth placed over this to exclude the light. The workers quickly discover the whereabouts of their queen and soon a stream of termites starts pouring into the nest and within a few hours they are all snugly installed in their new home. The king can be left to look after himself and he will find his own way to his usual position beside the queen. If there are any eggs present the workers will carry these into the nest, and the young will walk in of their own accord.

The large sheet of glass to cover the whole tray, in addition to the glass cover of the nest, is essential because the termites

are afraid to expose themselves to the open air, and the atmosphere in which they live must be kept humid. The half of the
tray not occupied by the cork nest serves as a chamber in
which the insects can run about freely and in which their food
can be placed; the glass cover prevents this food from drying
out too quickly. The question of the food that should be
supplied to them has already been dealt with in Chapter Ten,
page 65. It might be thought that the termites do not get
enough fresh air in a covered nest of this type, but such is not
the case. In fact, the first thing they do when they settle in
their new home is to plaster up every crack and cranny with
mound material and their excremental cement. Very soon you
see a narrow black rim appear round the edge of each cell,
where the glass touches it, and this is material that the termites
have pushed in to seal the cells. As has already been pointed
out, these insects flourish in an atmosphere that is heavy with
carbon dioxide and you have little to worry about ventilation,
so long as the nest is not hermetically sealed.

The reason for making the tray exactly twice the size of the
cork nest is for ease of manipulation. It is necessary from time
to time to remove the glass cover of the nest in order to clean it,
because the termites slowly coat the underside with excrement
in order to create a non-skid surface on which they can walk,
and this obscures the view. Also the investigator may wish to get
at the queen or other inhabitants without injuring the rest. If
the glass lid is removed and placed over the open half of the
tray and this is kept covered and darkened, whilst the nest
itself is left open and exposed, then all the termites will run
into the dark portion of the tray and any required manipulation
of the nest can be carried out without injuring the insects. As
soon as the nest is covered and darkened again, the termites
will return to it.

By means of such nests as these one can make many observations that would otherwise be impossible. Termites can be
kept alive and healthy in them for months, but they have some
disadvantages. They will only accommodate small colonies
with a few thousand inhabitants in each, and the termites are
not living under as natural conditions as might be desired. If
conditions as regards food and moisture are not quite to their

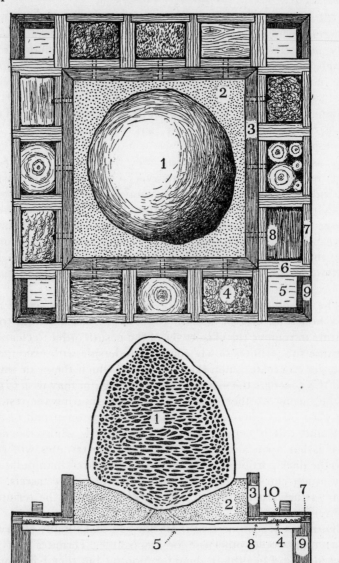

Fig. 38.—Diagram showing construction of stands for feeding experiments: (1) termite mound, (2) sand in box, (3) box for sand, (4) one of the food-chambers, (5) plate glass base, (6) wooden strips that form the food-chambers, (7) loose wooden strip for ease in cleaning food-chamber, (8) one of the entrances to the nest, (9) wooden stand, (10) cover to exclude light from food-chamber.

liking, they devour the eggs and young, and frequently they will murder the queen. The red mites described on page 82 often become troublesome and the hypopi may be so numerous as to hinder the movements of the termites. Nevertheless, with a little care and attention, I have kept nests such as these going for two years and more and have learned much from them.

In order to keep larger mounds in the laboratory, particularly for experiments on the feeding habits, a different type of apparatus was devised. A sheet of plate glass, eighteen inches square, is fixed on a wooden base about three inches high. Then a wooden frame, twelve inches square by three inches deep, is placed on the middle of the glass and round this twelve food-chambers, three along each side, are constructed of strips of wood as shown in the diagrams.

The size of the food-chambers is not important, but the termites will enter small chambers more freely than large ones. I chose the sizes four and a quarter inches by three and a quarter inches, and five inches by four inches, because I had a number of old photographic negatives which I could use as glass covers and these are very convenient as they are cut accurately square and to size. The wooden strips that form the food-chambers are three-eighths of an inch thick and of the same width and they are fixed firmly to the glass base by means of plastic resin glue. Before the strips and the centre box are fastened to the glass, grooves must be cut in the underside (as shown in Figure 38, 8) so that the termites can go in and out of the food-chambers.

The wooden box in the middle is now filled with clean sand, lightly moistened with water, and a termite mound of suitable size (about ten inches across at the base) is placed on the sand. After one or two days the insects will get over the shock of removal from the veld and will burrow through the sand and enter the food-chambers. All the investigator has to do after this is to put various food materials into the chambers and to watch the behaviour of the termites. Cardboard covers, with little wooden handles on them for convenience in handling, are placed over the food-chambers to exclude the light. Every other day the mound must be given a light spraying with water, otherwise it and the sand on which it stands may get too dry.

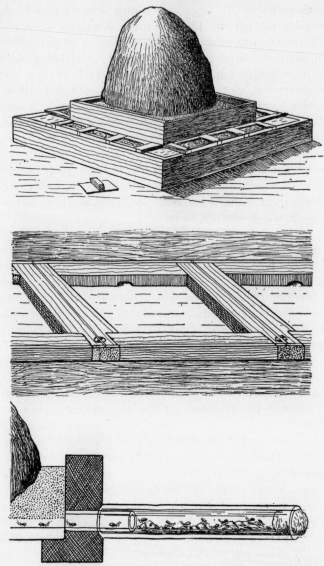

FIG. 39.—Stands for Feeding Experiments. Above, sketch of one of the stands with termite mound in position. In the middle, one of the food-chambers, $4\frac{1}{4}''$ by $3\frac{1}{4}''$ by $\frac{3}{8}''$ deep. Below, method of using glass tubes as food-containers, instead of the flat chambers.

A dozen or more stands of this type can be maintained in the laboratory with little trouble and all kinds of foodstuffs and attractants and repellants can be tested, as described in an earlier chapter. If the stands are kept in a part of the laboratory where the light is not too strong and where the direct rays of the sun never reach them, the cardboard covers to the food-chambers are not necessary as the termites soon learn to ignore the dim light and enter the chambers even though they are uncovered.

For some experiments it is necessary to have a large number of small containers in which many different types of food can be tested at once. For this purpose I made glass-bottomed boxes, with tubes projecting from the sides as shown in the diagram at the bottom of Figure 39. A stand eighteen inches square will comfortably accommodate forty such tubes, spaced one and a half inches apart along the sides, and such a stand is very useful for testing simultaneously a number of materials of which only small quantities are available, such as vitamins, amino-acids, drugs, and so on. The glass tubes, about six inches long by three-eighths of an inch internal diameter, slip easily on to the small tubes inserted in the wooden sides of the stand so that they can be removed without trouble for cleaning and replenishing. They have one serious disadvantage, however. The termites find the smooth surface of the glass too slippery for them and they coat the internal surface with their excrement and this obscures the view and means that the tubes have to be cleaned frequently. Furthermore, it is difficult to get the termites to leave the tubes when it is necessary to refill them. With the flat food-chambers there is no walking on the underside of the glass and the insects run inside the nest as soon as the glass lids are removed.

Often it is necessary to break up a mound in order to learn the condition of the inhabitants, to count them (see page 22), to remove the king and queen, or for some other purpose. If the broken pieces of the mound are put into the box on the middle of a stand and the termites are dumped on to them, they will repair their broken home, their first care being to close up all openings that might give access to enemies. Within two or three weeks they will reconstruct the ruined nest, making new cells and passages and binding the whole securely together.

Later, this can be broken up again if desired, to learn the results of any treatment, and the pieces put back again in the box, and the termites will repair it once more.

A colony can be divided up into four or five separate lots, in order to learn what happens when a few thousand workers are isolated with some short-winged grey nymphs, or with long-winged nymphs, or with eggs and young only. The lots must not be too small because they do not behave normally if they are split up into batches of only a few hundred in each; they simply shut themselves up in their cells and linger on for weeks until death overtakes them. There should be at least five thousand workers in each lot, and a larger number than this gives better results; the workers then set about the necessary repair work, forage for food, rear supplementary reproductives and generally do what they can to build up the colony once more.

Ordinary earthenware flower-pots, seven or eight inches in diameter, are very useful in dealing with batches taken from large mounds. The pots are filled with pieces of the broken mound and then five to ten thousand workers are put into each, together with the immature forms whose development is to be followed. The pots are then buried to about two-thirds their depth in a suitable spot in the garden and the termites are left to take care of themselves. It is essential that they should be protected from ants for the first two or three days, until they have had time to seal up all openings; dry sand poured on top of the broken mound in the pots helps to keep the ants out, and a sprinkling of ten per cent. D.D.T. powder round each pot completes the defence. Within a few days the termites will have made all secure for themselves and they need no further protection from their inveterate enemies. They enter the soil through the hole at the bottom of each pot and forage for food in the surrounding soil. All that the investigator now has to do is to remove the pots at intervals and examine the contents in order to learn what has happened to the termites. It is by this simple method that I secured numbers of supplementary reproductives.

Finally, in order to demonstrate another interesting habit of the termites, a different type of observation nest was devised. This is shown in Figure 40 and consists of plaster of Paris on a glass base. The wooden tray holding the glass base is half an inch deep and the glass measures eighteen inches by twenty-four inches. Four pieces of wood, four inches by three inches by half

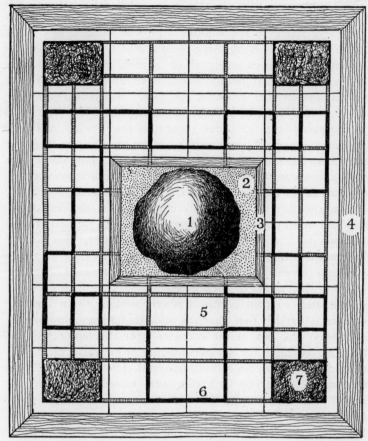

Fig. 40.—Apparatus to show how termites follow a trail in going to and from their home: (1) the mound, (2) sand, (3) box container, (4) frame of tray holding plaster of Paris with runways and food-chambers, on a glass base, (5) plaster of Paris with grooves cut in it for runways, (6) grooves painted with mound paste to form trail, (7) food-chamber. At first the termites follow the zig-zag route marked by the thick black line.

an inch, smeared with oil to prevent the plaster from sticking to them, are placed in each corner and another piece, eight inches by ten inches by half an inch, is put in the middle of the glass, and then the plaster of Paris is poured in to fill the tray level with the top of the frame, and quite flat. After the plaster has hardened the pieces of wood are removed and the four spaces in the corners form the food-chambers, whilst the larger space in the middle is for the wooden box, eight inches by ten inches by three inches, that holds the sand and the mound. Grooves an eighth of an inch wide and the same depth are cut in the plaster as shown in the diagram, to serve as runways for the termites, forming a network connecting the four food-chambers with the entrances to the nest. Old photographic negatives, five inches by four inches, with the gelatine cleaned off, were used to cover the plaster; these are more convenient than continuous sheets of glass along each side as they can be moved separately for cleaning or to get at any part of the plaster, without disturbing the rest.

A mound of suitable size is placed on sand in the central box. Lastly, a small portion of this mound is broken off and ground to a powder and made into a paste with water. This paste is then painted along the grooves as shown in the diagram, so as to form a devious track leading from one of the food-chambers to one of the entrances to the nest.

With such a set-up as this, it is very striking to see how the workers, when they first leave the mound and begin foraging for food, leave the box at the entrance near the figure 5 in the diagram, because the groove leading from this entrance is marked with their own mound material. They follow the long, devious route marked with this same material round to the food-chamber at 7, although there are much shorter ways for them to reach the food. Later, when they are more at home, they begin exploring the unmarked runways and within a few days they find the shorter routes and use them. On the other hand, they can be made to avoid certain of the runways altogether by painting them with material taken from mounds of other colonies. If two small mounds are placed side by side in the box of sand, it will be found that the members of each colony keep rigidly to their own runways and seal off the connections with those used by the other colony. After a few weeks, however, they may begin to mingle in the food-chambers and this may ventually lead to the two colonies combining into one large one.

# FURTHER READING

A most useful bibliography, listing all the publications of any importance about termites, from the first references to them in the year 1758, down to 1949, is "A Bibliography of the Isoptera (Termites)," by Francis J. Griffin, vol. 2, part 8, November, 1951, of *The Journal of the Society for the Bibliography of Natural History*, British Museum (Natural History), London.

The following books contain general accounts of termites:

EMERSON, A. E. and FISH, E., 1937. *Termite City*, pp. 127, 37 figs. Chicago.

IMMS, A. D., 1931. *Social Behaviour in Insects*, pp. 117, 20 figs. Methuen, London.

KOFOID, C. A. and others, 1946. *Termites and Termite Control*, pp. 795, 180 figs. University of California.

MAETERLINCK, M., 1928. *The Life of the White Ant*, pp. 206. Methuen, London.

MARAIS, E., 1937. *The Soul of the White Ant*, pp. 184. Methuen, London.

MICHENER, C. D., and MICHENER, M. H., 1951. *American Social Insects*, pp. 266, 109 figs. van Nostrand, New York.

NOYES, H., 1937. *Man and the Termite*, pp. 289, 8 plates. Davies, London.

RATCLIFFE, F. N., GAY, F. J., and GREAVES, T., 1952. *Australian Termites*, pp. 124, 21 figs. Council for Industrial and Scientific Research, Melbourne.

RICHARDS, O. W., 1953. *The Social Insects*, pp. 219, 12 figs. Macdonald, London.

SNYDER, T. E., 1935. *Our Enemy the Termite*, pp. 196, 56 figs. Comstock, Ithaca.

WHEELER, W. M., 1928. *The Social Insects*, pp. 378, 48 plates. Constable, London.

Two valuable publications in French are:

HEGH, E., 1922. *Les Termites*, pp. 756, 452 figs. Imprimerie Industrielle et Financiere, Brussels.

GRASSÉ, P. P., 1949. *Traité de Zoologie*, vol. 9, pp. 408 to 544, 100 figs. Masson et Cie, Paris.

# INDEX